ISO 9001:2000

Achieving Compliance and
Continuous Improvement in
Software Development
Companies

Also available from ASQ Quality Press:

Fundamental Concepts for the Software Quality Engineer
Taz Daughtrey

How to Audit the Process-Based QMS
Dennis R. Arter, Charles A. Cianfrani, and John E. (Jack) West

The ASQ ISO 9000:2000 Handbook
Joseph J. Tsiakals, Charles A. Cianfrani, and John E. (Jack) West

ISO 9001:2000 A Practical Quality Manual Explained
Kevin R. Grimes

Correct! Prevent! Improve! Driving Improvement through Problem Solving and Corrective and Preventive Action
Jeanne Ketola and Kathy Roberts

Software Quality Professional
SQP is a quarterly, peer-reviewed journal published by the American Society for Quality (ASQ). Its mission is to publish authoritative, practical articles that span the body of knowledge as defined for ASQ Certified Software Quality Engineers. Its content is intended to provide readers with significant information that contributes to their personal development and success in the software quality field. For more information or to subscribe, visit http://www.asq.org or call ASQ at 800-248-1946 or 414-272-8575.

To request a complimentary catalog of ASQ Quality Press publications, call (800) 248-1946, or visit our bookstore at http://www.asq.org.

ISO 9001:2000

Achieving Compliance and Continuous Improvement in Software Development Companies

Vivek (Vic) Nanda

ASQ Quality Press
Milwaukee, Wisconsin

American Society for Quality, Quality Press, Milwaukee 53203

© 2003 by ASQ

All rights reserved. Published 2003

Printed in the United States of America

12 11 10 09 08 07 06 05 04 03   5 4 3 2 1

Library of Congress Cataloging-in-Publication Data

Nanda, Vivek.
  ISO 9001:2000 achieving complaince and continuous improvement in
software development companies / Vivek (Vic) Nanda.
    p. cm.
  Includes bibliographical references and index.
  ISBN 0-87389-594-0 (Hardcover, Case Bound : alk. paper)
  1. Computer software—Quality control. 2. ISO 9000 Series Standards.
I. Title.

QA76.76.Q35N35 2003
005.1—dc22   2003016774

Publisher: William A. Tony
Acquisitions Editor: Annemieke Hytinen
Project Editor: Paul O'Mara
Production Administrator: Barbara Mitrovic
Special Marketing Representative: Robin Barry

ASQ Mission: The American Society for Quality advances individual,
organizational, and community excellence worldwide through learning,
quality improvement, and knowledge exchange.

Attention Bookstores, Wholesalers, Schools, and Corporations: ASQ Quality
Press books, videotapes, audiotapes, and software are available at quantity
discounts with bulk purchases for business, educational, or instructional use.
For information, please contact ASQ Quality Press at 800-248-1946, or write to
ASQ Quality Press, P.O. Box 3005, Milwaukee, WI 53201-3005.

To place orders or to request a free copy of the ASQ Quality Press Publications
Catalog, including ASQ membership information, call 800-248-1946. Visit our
Web site at www.asq.org or http://qualitypress.asq.org.

 Printed on acid-free paper

Quality Press
600 N. Plankinton Avenue
Milwaukee, Wisconsin 53203
Call toll free 800-248-1946
Fax 414-272-1734
www.asq.org
http://qualitypress.asq.org
http://standardsgroup.asq.org
E-mail: authors@asq.org

This book is dedicated to my loving parents, Hari Om and Versha, for their constant encouragement and support of all my endeavors.

Table of Contents

Acknowledgments

First of all, I would like to thank my wonderful wife, Dipti, for her motivation, constant support, patience, and understanding while I pursued my passion to write and bring this book to market. Dipti, my deepest thanks.

I would also like to take this opportunity to thank my colleagues in the industry, both past and present, from whom I have learned and continue to learn about disciplined software engineering practices aimed at enhancing product quality and customer satisfaction. Special thanks to Mr. Shawn Osborne, president and CEO of Ulticom, who has been a very enthusiastic supporter of my efforts in writing this book. Special thanks are also due to my friend and mentor, Prof. Nazim H. Madhavji, for instilling in me the desire to write and speak about my industry experiences, and to continue to actively contribute to the software engineering body of knowledge.

I am grateful to the reviewers of ASQ Quality Press and to Bob Davis who provided me their valuable suggestions. Thanks to Annemieke Hytinen, Paul O'Mara, Robin Barry, ASQ Quality Press staff associated with this project, and Leayn and Paul Tabili of New Paradigm for their help in transforming my dreams into reality with the publication of this book. Finally, I would like to take this opportunity to thank all my relatives and friends whose best wishes and words of encouragement have been a valuable source of strength, and have contributed to my personal drive to accomplish this project.

Preface

Historically, in spite of the abundance of books offering ISO 9000 implementation advice, the software development industry has struggled in understanding and interpreting the standard's requirements for its use. Unfortunately, this trend continues with the release of the ISO 9001:2000 standard. Why is it so?

The answer is not difficult to find. As is well known, ISO 9000 requirements are intentionally *generically* worded, so that they may apply equally well to, say, a tire manufacturer or a software development organization. For the most part, the generic wording of ISO 9000 requirements has not caused much difficulty to manufacturing or service companies in understanding and applying the requirements to their business. However, due to the unique nature of the software development process (in that it markedly differs from a shop-floor-oriented manufacturing process), the software industry has often regarded the ISO 9000 standards as difficult to interpret and implement. For example, while most companies would find interpreting the requirement pertaining to "control of nonconforming product" as trivial, it is not so for the software industry. This is because unlike a damaged bulb or a damaged tire that can be clearly labeled and easily segregated to prevent unintentional use, software code is comparatively less tangible, and therefore, labeling and segregating defective software is more challenging. Similarly, what does the requirement pertaining to "calibration of measuring equipment" mean to a software development organization?

This book has been written to help demystify ISO 9001:2000 requirements for software development. All discussions and examples are in the vocabulary and context of software development organizations. There are many reasons why this book is unique. Let me now point out some of the salient features of this book:

• First, unlike most *generic* ISO 9000 books on the market, this book provides detailed ISO 9001:2000 requirements explanation and interpretation specifically for the software development industry (in accordance with

ISO 90003). ISO 90003 is a guideline document provided by ISO, and it provides interpretation advice on ISO 9001:2000 for the software industry.

- Second, unlike other ISO 9000 guide books that merely provide an explanation of *what* the standard's requirements mean, this book also provides detailed guidance on *how* a software development organization can comply with a stated requirement. In other words, this book is like a handy consultant telling you what needs to be done and how to do it!

- Third, in addition to demystifying ISO 9001:2000 requirements, this book provides guidance on how to plan and execute a successful ISO 9001:2000 implementation project. The importance of this should not be overlooked. A sound implementation strategy for planning, tracking, and controlling the ISO 9001:2000 implementation project is a critical element of a successful ISO 9000 implementation.

- Finally, this book provides extensive guidance on how to successfully navigate the ISO 9000 registration audit process, including issues such as ISO 9000 registrar selection and tips for audit preparation and audit management.

This book will serve as an indispensable guide not only for software development companies that are pursuing an ISO 9000 registration, but also for those that are already registered to the standard. This is because the content in this book will help stimulate discussion on alternative ways in which your organization can comply with a stated requirement. This may help you improve upon your current implementation, which is bound to have room for improvement in certain areas. Due to the in-depth explanation of requirements, ISO 9000–registered companies will likely discover requirements the complete implications and interpretations of which they may not have yet addressed in their quality management system (QMS)! Moreover, ideas presented in this book can help an ISO 9000–registered organization *augment* its continuous improvement mechanisms.

This book will also serve as a valuable reference text for software engineering students in colleges and universities because they will gain insight into how software development companies establish QMSs. This information will answer their questions about "how things happen in the software industry" with regards to implementation of quality practices. Therefore, this valuable insight will better prepare them to make the transition from academia to the software industry. That is, this book will serve as a bridge between their understanding of academic concepts related to software quality and the "real-life" implementation of quality practices in software development companies.

In writing this book, I have assumed that the readers either have experience in the software development industry or have a general understanding of software engineering practices via formal education. However, no prior experience in ISO 9000 is required or assumed. I have taken utmost care to present the book's contents in the most simple and straightforward manner possible and I have avoided use of fancy jargon. I am confident that this book will serve as an indispensable handbook for software development organizations as they work on establishing and continuously improving an ISO 9001:2000–compliant quality management system.

Vivek (Vic) Nanda, CSQE, CQA

1

Introduction

W hat is ISO 9000? What is ISO 9001:2000? How can your organization benefit from an ISO 9000 registration? This chapter provides answers to such fundamental questions pertaining to ISO 9000. It serves as a quick introduction to ISO 9001:2000, its relevance, and its relationship to the ISO 9000 family of standards. A description of key terms in ISO 9000 is also provided. Familiarity with these terms is essential for your correct understanding and implementation of the standard's requirements. Finally, this chapter describes how this book is structured, and who should read which chapters.

INTRODUCTION TO ISO 9000

The International Organization for Standardization (ISO) is a worldwide federation of national standards bodies[1] from more than 140 countries, one from each country. ISO was established in 1947 and its mission is to promote the development of standardization and related activities in the world with a view to facilitating the international exchange of goods and services, and to develop cooperation in the spheres of intellectual, scientific, technological, and economic activity.

All the member countries of ISO work together in technical committees (TC) to create international standards. In 1979, ISO formed a technical committee with the objective of establishing a generic set of quality management standards. In 1987, ISO/TC 176 authored the first release of the ISO 9000 family of documents. Since then, based on industry input and lessons learned from its use, ISO/TC 176 has continually improved the ISO 9000 family of documents. The next major release of the ISO 9000 family of documents was in 1994, followed by the latest and most significantly enhanced release on December 15, 2000.[2] The 1994 release of the ISO 9000 standards is often referred to as "ISO 9001:1994," while the year 2000 release is referred to as "ISO 9001:2000" or "ISO 9000:2000."

ISO 9000 Family of Documents

ISO 9000 is a family of international quality management standards and guidelines containing standardized requirements for an organization's quality management system (QMS). ISO 9000 is applicable to all organizations, irrespective of their type, size, or product category. In essence, the ISO 9000 family is a collection of good management practices that enable an organization to meet or exceed the quality requirements of its customer(s). Therefore, ISO 9000 is a vehicle any organization can use for achieving customer satisfaction.

As stated in the preface, in order to accommodate all types of companies and industries, ISO 9000 requirements are intentionally generically worded. In addition, ISO 9000 is *nonprescriptive,* that is, its requirements state *what* practices you must implement in your organization, but the requirements do not specify *how* you must implement those practices (implementation is left to the discretion of the organization). The guiding principle at all times is that no matter what implementation your organization chooses, in the end your implementation must satisfactorily meet the *intent* of the ISO 9000 requirement.

Table 1.1 shows the key documents of the ISO 9000:2000 family.

ISO 9001:2000 and ISO 9004:2000 are together referred to as the "consistent pair." This is because they are structured in the same format and use the same terminology. The alignment of these two documents was done to enable companies to easily use both the documents as an integrated pair. For this purpose, both the documents have identically numbered clauses and titles. It is strongly recommended that an organization first comply with the requirements contained in ISO 9001:2000. Having established a sound QMS, it can then implement the practices contained in ISO 9004:2000 for enhancing the effectiveness of its QMS. Keep in mind that an organization that has successfully implemented the practices in ISO 9004:2000 cannot be

Table 1.1   Key documents of the ISO 9000:2000 family.

Standard/Guideline	Content
ISO 9000:2000, Quality Management Systems— Fundamentals and Vocabulary	Contains definitions of key terms used in the ISO 9000 family of documents.
ISO 9001:2000, Quality Management Systems— Requirements	Contains all the requirements that must be implemented by an organization in order to be registered to ISO 9001:2000. ☞ This is the only document in the ISO 9000 family of documents against which an organization can be audited and registered.[3] ☞ ISO 9001:2000 replaces ISO 9001:1994, ISO 9002:1994, and ISO 9003:1994. Consequently, any organization previously registered to the 1994 edition of the ISO 9000 standards must upgrade its registration to ISO 9001:2000 by December 15, 2003.
ISO 9004:2000, Quality Management Systems— Guidelines for Performance Improvements	Contains recommended practices that an organization should implement in order to achieve continuous process improvement. The use of this document is optional. This document is primarily intended for those companies that wish to develop their QMS beyond the minimum requirements contained in ISO 9001:2000.

registered to ISO 9004:2000; this is because no such registration is available. However, ISO 9004:2000 is a tool that an organization can use to achieve its own business goals, such as gaining recognition as an industry leader through national quality award programs.

Supporting Documents of the ISO 9000 Family

Besides the ISO 9000 family, ISO/TC 176 has authored an ISO 10000 family of documents that contains additional guidance and requirements for specific applications. The ISO 10000 documents are primarily intended as "supporting documents" to the ISO 9000 family. To obtain the list of these documents, refer to the bibliography section in the ISO 9001:2000 standard.

Obtaining Official Copies of ISO 9000 Documents

Any organization implementing a QMS as per ISO 9000 requirements *must* purchase official copies of the standard. This is because ISO documents are protected by copyright, and therefore, use of photocopies is prohibited. In fact, organizations are cautioned that unofficial copies of the standard or of other ISO guideline documents, if found during an organization's registration audit, will almost certainly cause an audit nonconformance to be reported against the organization. Official copies of all ISO documents referenced in this book can be obtained from:

American Society for Quality (ASQ)
600 North Plankinton Avenue
PO Box 3005
Milwaukee, WI 53203-3005 USA
Phone: 800-248-1946, 414-272-8575 (outside the United States,
    Canada, Mexico)
Fax: 414-272-1734
e-mail: help@asq.org

American National Standards Institute (ANSI)
25 West 43rd Street, 4th Floor
New York, NY 10036 USA
Phone: 212-642-4900
Fax: 212-398-0023
e-mail: info@ansi.org

BENEFITS OF ISO 9000 REGISTRATION

According to ISO,[4] by December 31, 2001, the number of ISO 9000 registrations had reached an astounding 510,616 registrations in 161 countries, up from 408,631 registrations in 157 countries at the end of December 2000, and the number continues to grow! Organizations registered to the ISO 9000 standard include both public and private companies belonging to the manufacturing and service sectors. In addition, numerous organizations have chosen not to be formally registered to the standard but have nonetheless implemented their QMS as per ISO 9000 requirements and have claimed a self-declared compliance to the standard. While such self-declared compliance is always questionable, it clearly demonstrates that ISO 9000 has established itself as the most popular international quality benchmark. Why? The answer is simple—ISO 9000 quality requirements make "plain good sense." Fundamentally, ISO 9000 is the basis for delivering quality products and services. At the same time, it is not a panacea for all problems facing an organization. However, it does provide an organization the basic infrastructure to facilitate improvements in organizational processes, and enables the organization to become more effective and efficient.

In order to further the popularity of ISO 9000, in the year 2000 revision of the standard, ISO/TC 176 has addressed a major misunderstanding regarding ISO 9000. It has often been argued that ISO 9000 fosters excessive documentation. ISO/TC 176 has addressed this criticism by significantly reducing the documentation requirements in the year 2000 version of the standard. Further, they have stressed that ISO 9000 requires (and always *has* required) a "documented quality management system," and not a "system of documents."

Some of the key benefits of an ISO 9000 registration for an organization are:

1. It enables the organization to gain competitive advantage due to it being perceived as a "best in class" supplier by its customers. Consequently, this enables the organization to retain current customers, attract new customers, increase market share, and enhance top-line revenue growth.

2. It fosters continuous improvement in the organization's productivity, on-time delivery performance, and within-budget project execution. Consequently, this enables the organization to improve its bottom line.

3. It enables the organization to bid on tenders that require ISO 9000 registered supplier(s). Increasingly, before establishing a business relationship with a potential supplier, potential customers inquire about the existence of a formal QMS in the initial request for information (RFI) questionnaire. Therefore, an organization that has established a QMS as per ISO 9000 requirements enjoys tremendous advantage when responding to customer RFIs.

4. It provides customers a high degree of assurance regarding the organization's QMS because of the fact that the organization was independently audited by an accredited registrar.

5. It increases consistency in project execution due to the use of the same processes across multiple projects.

6. It reduces the organization's reliance on "heroes" to make projects a success because all employees[5] are aware of the required quality practices.

7. It reduces (or eliminates) the organization's dependence on a few individuals for information regarding critical processes because such processes are formally documented.

8. It reduces wastage of resources in rejection and rework of inferior quality products due to continuous improvement of the processes. Consequently, this enables the organization to shift from a reactive mode of operation (performing corrective action) to a proactive mode (performing preventive action).

Finally, bear in mind that implementation of ISO 9000 requirements will result in changes to the organization's processes. During the period of transition from the old processes to the new and modified processes, a temporary decrease in performance efficiency in the affected areas may occur as employees familiarize themselves with the new way of working. Also, the requirement to perform additional tasks in certain processes in order to comply with ISO 9000 requirements may add to the time required to execute those processes. For example, the organization may not have previously verified its software design prior to coding, which it would now have to do in order to comply with ISO 9000 requirements. This would therefore require the additional task of design review to be performed in the software design phase. It is important to not regard such additional tasks executed to facilitate delivery of a quality product or service as an overhead. Instead, such tasks should be viewed as a *necessary* part of the process that the organization had previously not performed. Furthermore, execution of such tasks should be viewed as a necessary investment in quality to reap long-term benefits in the form improved quality of product(s) and service(s), improved customer satisfaction, savings in the form of less rework required to fix defective products, and continuous improvements in organizational effectiveness and efficiency.

ABOUT THIS BOOK

This book complements the *ISO 9001:2000, Quality Management Systems—Requirements* standard. It should be used *along with* the ISO 9001:2000 document as you work toward your goal. Simply stated, the ISO 9001:2000 standard will tell you *what* are the requirements that you must meet in order to comply with the standard, and this book will serve as an everyday "implementation guide" that explains *how* you can comply with those requirements.

The following section describes key terms that are used throughout the book. It provides an overview of how the book's chapters are organized, and recommends who should read which chapters.

Key Terms You Should Know

Table 1.2 provides a description of some key terms that you will encounter throughout ISO 9001:2000. For the official definition of the complete set of terms used in the ISO 9000 documents, refer to *ANSI/ISO/ASQ Q9000:2000— Quality management standards—Fundamentals and vocabulary.*[6]

Table 1.2 Description of key ISO 9000 terms.

Term	Description
Organization	A company, enterprise, or institution (private or public) that provides a product to a customer. In other words, the term organization refers to "you"—the entity seeking ISO 9000 registration.
Supplier	Supplies a product or service to the organization. The supplied product may be included as part of the end product delivered by the organization. In this book, the term *subcontractor* is also used to refer to a supplier who has been subcontracted software development work by the organization.
Customer	Receives the product provided by the organization.
Product	The result of processes or activities. 👉 Throughout this book, wherever the term "product" appears, it can also mean service. This is consistent with the usage of the term "product" in ISO 9001:2000.
Process	The sequence of activities executed to transform input(s) to output(s).
Procedure	A documented description of a process. A procedure states "what" the activities in a process are and it includes a brief description of each activity. Procedures are primarily intended for communicating high-level information about a process. Note: Most organizations typically augment their procedures with underlying "work instructions" that are more detailed and describe "how" the activities described in the procedure are executed. Therefore, work instructions are primarily intended for use by process practitioners—employees involved in the daily execution of a process.
Record	An evidence of activity performed or results achieved.
Quality manual	A document describing the QMS of an organization.
Quality management system (QMS)	An organization's QMS encompasses its processes, resources, procedures, and records for quality planning, quality control, quality assurance, and continuous quality improvement.
Shall	Indicates a mandatory requirement that must be met. All organizations, irrespective of their size or type of business, must comply with this requirement. 👉 In this book, most occurrences of the term *must* refer to an explicit mandatory (shall) requirement in ISO 9001:2000. In some instances, it may be used to refer to something that is otherwise necessary.
Should[7]	Indicates a requirement, compliance to which is recommended but not mandatory. 👉 Most implementation guidance in this book contains *should* statements because this book presents one or more possible ways of complying with an ISO 9001:2000 requirement, and use of any one particular solution is not specifically mandatory. 👉 In the event that a requirement identified as a *"should"* in this book conflicts with the same requirement identified as a *"shall"* in ISO 9001:2000, ISO 9001:2000 shall carry precedence.

In addition to these ISO 9000 terms, the following terms are used throughout this book:

- *Quality management system documentation.* QMS documentation refers to documentation that is within the scope of an organization's QMS. For an ISO 9001:2000–compliant organization, this includes documents that are explicitly required per subclause 4.2.1 of ISO 9001:2000, as well as those documents that are created by the organization to ensure effective planning, operation, and control of its processes. Examples of QMS documentation include: quality policy, quality manual, quality objectives, procedures, records, forms, templates, checklists, project and product documentation, and records.

- *Quality control.* Quality control comprises activities that are executed to fulfill quality requirements. This includes activities to monitor a process to ensure its output is of required quality, as well as activities to correct discrepancies when they occur.

- *Quality assurance.* Quality assurance comprises activities that when executed provide sufficient confidence that the resulting product will comply with applicable quality requirements.

- *Project documentation.* Project documentation refers to all internal company documentation and records that are produced during the course of a product development project, beginning with the requirements document for the product, and ending with documentation authorizing release of the product. Other examples of project documentation include software requirements specification (SRS), software design document (SDD), verification records, validation records, test plans, and so on.

- *Product documentation.* Product documentation refers to documentation that describes product installation and use, and is prepared primarily for delivery to the customer. Product documentation may also be referred to as user documentation, user manuals, or product manuals. Examples of product documentation include product installation and configuration manual(s), product user's guide, product troubleshooting guide, and so on.

- *Registration (or certification).* The assessment by a third-party accredited registrar of an organization's QMS against the requirements of the ISO 9001:2000 standard and the subsequent issuance of a certificate to confirm conformance of the organization with the standard's requirements is known as "registration" or "certification."

- *Self-declared compliance.* This is an increasingly observed practice wherein an organization claims that it has implemented a QMS as per ISO 9000 requirements. This may be as a result of the organization passing an internal quality audit, performed either by its internal quality assurance personnel or by a consulting company. However, an independent assessment was not made by an accredited registrar to verify this claim. In the worst examples of self-declared compliance, companies have been known to claim compliance to ISO 9000 when not even a single internal quality audit had been performed! Due to the obvious "self-declared" nature of this compliance, such compliance is always less desirable and questionable when compared to a formal ISO 9000 registration. However, if an organization has truly implemented a QMS that complies with ISO 9000 requirements and this has been confirmed during audits performed by the organization's customers, then such self-declared compliance is surely better than not implementing a QMS at all! If the customer(s) found the supplier's "unregistered" QMS satisfactory, then it meets the key objective of ISO 9000—meeting customers' requirements and achieving customer satisfaction.

• *Accreditation.* Accreditation is the procedure that an authoritative body uses to formally recognize that an organization (for example, an ISO 9000 registrar) is competent to carry out activities pertaining to its business. Accreditation, which is strictly voluntary, provides assurance to a registrar's customers that the registrar operates in accordance with internationally accepted criteria. The national accreditation body of each country provides accreditation to the country's registrars to perform registration audits to different standards. In the United States, for example, registrars who perform audits to ISO 9000 may obtain accreditation under the National Accreditation Program jointly conducted by the American National Standards Institute (ANSI) and the Registrar Accreditation Board (RAB).

• *Registrar.* An independent body that verifies whether an organization has successfully implemented the requirements of the applicable quality standard, and subsequently issues a certificate confirming the same, is called a registrar or registration body. Examples of ISO 9000 registrars are: British Standards Institute (BSI), Bureau Veritas Quality International (BVQI), Lloyd's Register Quality Assurance (LRQA), Société Genéralé de Surveillance (SGS), Det Norske Veritas Certification (DNV), Quality Management Institute (QMI), KEMA, and Underwriters Laboratories (UL).

Figure 1.1 illustrates the terms described previously.

• *Continuous improvement or continual improvement?* ISO 9001:2000 uses the term "continual improvement" instead of the term "continuous improvement" widely used in the software industry. This is because TC 176 members agreed that although from a pure quality philosophy, organizations should seek continuous improvement, all organizations may not be able to demonstrate an incessant set of improvement actions (implied by *continuous*

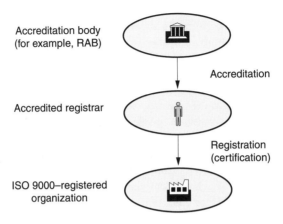

Accreditation body
(for example, RAB)

Accreditation

Accredited registrar

Registration
(certification)

ISO 9000–registered
organization

Figure 1.1 Relationship between accreditation body, registrar, and ISO 9000–registered organization.

improvement), but they may be able to demonstrate discrete improvement actions (*continual* improvement). In order to accommodate both views, the term "continual improvement" is used throughout this book when a specific ISO 9001:2000 requirement is paraphrased or explained, while the term "continuous improvement" is used in all other cases (where appropriate). For most readers, however, who are not concerned about such subtleties, the terms may be regarded as being equivalent.

• *ISO 9000 registration or ISO 9001:2000 registration?* As stated in Table 1.1, with the year 2000 revision of the ISO 9000 family of documents, the only ISO 9000 document against which an organization can be audited and registered is *ISO 9001: Quality Management Systems— Requirements.* Before the year 2000, an organization could obtain registration to any of the three ISO 9000 standards: ISO 9001:1994, ISO 9002:1994, or ISO 9003:1994. Many authors, myself included, often refer to an ISO registration simply as "ISO 9000 registration." It does not really matter whether an ISO registration is referred to as ISO 9000 registration or ISO 9001:2000 registration, as long as the reader is aware of the exact meaning (as explained here).

Finally, bear in mind that the ISO 9001:2000 standard contains several subjectively worded requirements. Some of the subjective words used in the standard are: "necessary," "appropriate," "suitable," and so on. Such subjective wording of the requirements provides different organizations the flexibility to determine the formality and rigor of their ISO 9000 implementation so that the implementation meets each organization's requirements and its customer requirements. On the other hand, such subjective wording may also result in a different interpretation of the same requirement by organizations and their auditors.

Organization of This Book

Chapter 2 provides an overview of ISO 9001:2000 requirements. Chapter 3 describes the recommended approach for implementing an ISO 9001:2000–compliant QMS for the first time. Chapters 4 through 8 explain the respective requirements clauses in ISO 9001:2000. Finally, chapter 9 describes the ISO 9000 registration process, provides guidance on how to select a registrar, and provides tips for audit preparation and audit management. Appendixes A, B, and C include sample QMS documentation and typical auditor questions for each of the ISO 9001:2000 requirements clauses. Appendix D describes the acronyms used in this book.

Who Should Read Which Chapters

Table 1.3 provides guidance on who should read which chapters of this book. Note that this guidance also applies to companies that may be working toward a self-declared compliance only, with the exception that such companies may omit reading Chapter 9.

Table 1.3   Who should read which chapters.

Reader Type	Recommended Reading
• Management representative • Quality practitioners (for example, quality engineers, quality analysts, quality consultants, quality trainers, and so on)	All chapters and appendixes
Middle managers (and higher)	Chapters 1 and 2, Chapter 3 ("Getting Started" section), Chapters 4 through 8 (relevant clauses only)
Department managers and staff	Chapters 1 and 2, Chapter 3 ("Getting Started" section), Chapters 4 through 8, Appendix B (relevant documents only), and Appendix C
ISO 9000 auditors	Chapters 4 through 8, and Appendix C
Software engineering and software quality students	Chapter 1 through 8, Chapter 9 (optional), Appendixes A and B

ENDNOTES

1. List of national standards bodies of all member countries of ISO can be obtained from www.iso.ch. As an example, United States is represented by the American National Standards Institute (ANSI).
2. ANSI/ISO/ASQ. *ANSI/ISO/ASQ Q9001-2000: Quality management systems—requirements.* Milwaukee: ASQ Quality Press, 2002.
3. Throughout this book, paragraphs that are tagged with the hand icon ( ) are meant to draw the reader's attention to an important piece of information, such as a pertinent clarification, recommended approach, or to caution the reader about pitfalls.
4. ISO Survey. *The ISO survey of ISO 9000 and ISO 14000 certificates, 11th cycle.* Geneva, Switzerland: International Organization for Standardization, 2001.
5. Throughout this book, the word *employee* is used to refer to any individual working for the organization, regardless of whether the person works full-time or part-time, and regardless of whether the person is permanent, temporary, or on contract.
6. ANSI/ISO/ASQ. *ANSI/ISO/ASQ Q9000-2000: Quality managment standards—fundamentals and vocabulary.* Milwaukee: ASQ Quality Press, 2002.
7. Note that in ISO 9001:2000 there is only one "should" requirement (included as a Note under Clause 4.1).

2

Understanding
ISO 9001:2000

This chapter describes key enhancements included in the ISO 9001:2000 standard. A discussion of these key enhancements is required for two reasons. First, being familiar with these key enhancements will help you understand how the standard has evolved. As a result, you will better understand how the expectations of ISO 9000 auditors have evolved because of these changes. Second, for those of you who are familiar with the previous version of ISO 9000 (that is, ISO 9001:1994), this discussion will enable you to better plan your migration to ISO 9001:2000 by focusing on the most significant changes. This chapter also includes a high-level overview of all the requirements clauses in ISO 9001:2000. The purpose of the requirements overview section is to provide you with a comprehensive understanding of the breadth of the standard's requirements so that you can better plan your implementation. This chapter concludes with an introduction to ISO 90003 and explains the relevance of this guideline document to the software industry.

KEY CHANGES FROM ISO 9001:1994 TO ISO 9001:2000

As we entered the new millennium in December 2000, so did ISO 9000 with the release of the year 2000 version of the standard. This revision to the ISO 9000 standard is the most radical to date, and it was necessitated by deficiencies identified from the use of its previous version. This section describes key enhancements in ISO 9001:2000. Before describing these enhancements, it is worthwhile to briefly discuss the rationale for such a major revision of the standard.

Since the mid-1990s, there has been a gradual but noticeable paradigm shift in the quality field. Increasingly, organizations are beginning to discuss and assess quality in the context of their business processes. This has led to a shift in management style from department or people management to *process management.* Consequently, "process improvement" is increasingly used as a synonym for "quality improvement" or "continuous improvement." Why? There is a growing realization of the obvious, that all work in an organization gets accomplished through the execution of business processes. As stated in chapter 1, a process is a "sequence of activities executed to transform input(s) to output(s)." Therefore, improvement in the quality of a product is largely dictated by the process used to produce it. Simply stated, a high-quality process will deliver a high-quality output. Therefore, all the business processes of an organization taken together as a whole will deliver a high-quality product, provided that all the individual business processes are sufficiently mature. This widely accepted premise is the cornerstone of the new and improved ISO 9000 standard.

In addition to the above fundamental change in how we view quality, there have been some well-known criticisms of the ISO 9000 standard as well. Addressing each of these criticisms in ISO 9001:2000 constituted a key objective for ISO/TC 176. Some of these criticisms were:

- ISO 9000 stresses conformance to documented procedures, and thus fosters maintenance of the status quo as opposed to encouraging continuous improvement.

- ISO 9000 entails excessive documentation and does not provide an organization the discretion to determine how much documentation is sufficient for it to deliver a quality product.

- Quantitative process improvement is key to sustaining and improving quality, yet ISO 9000 embodies minimal requirements for use of measurements to control and improve processes.

- ISO 9000 lacks requirements pertaining to monitoring of customer satisfaction. Consequently, an organization implementing ISO 9000 has limited visibility into the impact, or lack thereof, of its improvement activities on its customers.

With the objective of addressing the aforementioned deficiencies in the ISO 9000 standard, ISO/TC 176 started work on the year 2000 version of the standard. ISO/TC 176 recognized that before beginning work on the revisions to the ISO 9000 requirements, it needed to establish a set of quality management principles that would form the underpinnings of the revised standard. A set of eight quality management principles was developed based on the experience and knowledge of the international quality experts in ISO/TC 176, and by studying the quality management principles most widely used around the world. While these eight quality management principles are not explicitly stated in ISO 9001:2000, they do appear in ISO 9000:2000 and ISO 9004:2000. Each requirement in ISO 9001:2000 is founded on one of these principles:

1. *Customer-focused organization.* An organization's success is contingent upon it retaining current customers and attracting new ones. Therefore, in order to achieve customer satisfaction, an organization must understand current and future requirements of its customers, and it must continuously strive to exceed customer expectations.

2. *Leadership.* Organizational success requires a strong leadership that has a clear vision and is committed to the organization's goals and objectives.

3. *Involvement of people.* In order to ensure organizational success, it is vital that each employee be involved and contribute to the best of his or her ability.

4. *Process approach.* Because all work in organizations is executed in processes, improvements are easier to implement by taking a *process view* of the organization.

5. *System approach to management.* All the processes in an organization interact in order to deliver the end product of the organization. Therefore, an organization cannot improve quality by merely looking at individual processes in isolation. It must improve the interaction and handoff *across* processes because a poor interface between different processes may have a debilitating impact on overall process execution.

6. *Continual improvement.* In order to be recognized as one of the better organizations amongst its peers, every organization must strive to distinguish itself. This can only happen by establishing continual improvement as a permanent objective.

7. *Factual approach to decision making.* Informed decisions can only be made based on facts and data. Therefore, every organization must strive to maintain useful, complete, and accurate data for use in its decision-making process.

8. *Mutually beneficial supplier relationships.* An organization's ability to deliver quality products is based upon its ability to establish a synergistic and quality-driven relationship with its suppliers.

The key enhancements to ISO 9001:2000, founded on these principles, are as follows:

Revised Structure

ISO 9001:2000 groups all the standard's requirements under five major clauses as opposed to the 20 elements contained in ISO 9001:1994. These clauses are:

- *Quality management system (clause 4).* This includes general requirements and documentation requirements that are applicable to the entire QMS.

- *Management responsibility (clause 5).* This entails providing direction, setting goals and objectives, and management review of the QMS.

- *Resource management (clause 6).* This entails determining resource needs, and providing and managing the resources during the course of the project.

- *Product realization (clause 7).* This entails transforming the input (customer requirements) into output (product and/or service) by means of processes, such that the output meets customer requirements and expectations.

- *Measurement, analysis, and improvement (clause 8).* "Measurement" entails defining and collecting measurements for continual improvement (including customer satisfaction data), and performing internal quality audits. "Analysis" entails examining the collected measurement data and audit results to identify trends and opportunities for improvement. "Improvement" entails management review and use of the audit results and measurement data for the formulation and implementation of improvement plans.

This cycle of "management responsibility → resource management → product realization → measurement, analysis, and improvement" repeats itself in successive iterations and thus results in continuous improvement within the organization.

Process Approach

Due to the widely prevalent "process management approach" in today's businesses, ISO 9001:2000 embodies a process-based structure. This significant shift from the 20 requirements elements–based structure in ISO 9001:1994 necessitates a new approach to implementing ISO 9000 requirements. Organizations now have to approach their QMS implementation as the interplay of organizational processes, both departmental and cross-functional (across departments). ISO 9001:2000 requires that the processes in the QMS be identified, along with their sequence and interaction. Further, the organization must manage, measure, analyze, and continually improve the processes in its QMS.

Increased Emphasis on Management Commitment

ISO 9001:2000 places increased emphasis on the role of senior management in the establishment of the QMS. Senior management must establish the quality policy, set measurable objectives, and conduct regular management reviews. While these management responsibilities existed in ISO 9001:1994 as well, ISO 9001:2000 has introduced minor enhancements or added new requirements pertaining to these activities. For example, clause 5.1, Management Commitment, now states that senior management is responsible for demonstrating its commitment to the QMS by continually emphasizing to employees the importance of meeting customer and regulatory requirements. New requirements now place the onus on senior management to ensure that all customer requirements are determined and met. ISO 9001:2000 also includes new input and output requirements for management reviews.

Emphasis on Customer Satisfaction and Continual Improvement

ISO 9001:2000 requires an organization to measure and continually monitor customer perception of whether the organization has met customer requirements. Furthermore, it must analyze the collected data and formulate improvement plans for increasing customer satisfaction.

The standard now contains explicit requirements for continual improvement as opposed to implicit ones in ISO 9001:1994. Organizations are required to continually improve the effectiveness of their QMS as per their quality policy and quality objectives, and by using the following vehicles: quality audits, measurement data, corrective action, preventive action, and management reviews.

Emphasis on Measurement-Driven Performance Improvement

A significant enhancement in ISO 9001:2000 is the increased emphasis placed on performance measurement, measurement data analysis, and continual improvement of products and processes. This includes measurement of customer satisfaction data as well as supplier performance data. Furthermore, data pertaining to process performance and product conformity are also required as an input to management reviews. As opposed to ISO 9001:1994, which merely required that use of statistical techniques be *considered*, ISO 9001:2000 *requires* use of statistical techniques for continual process improvement. Organizations, however, are provided the freedom to determine which statistical techniques are appropriate for use and where to use them.

Revised Documentation Requirements

There is a significant reduction in the documentation requirements of the revised standard. ISO has emphasized that ISO 9000 requires *(and always has required)* a "documented quality management system" and not a "system of documents." ISO 9001:2000 provides an organization much more freedom to determine how much QMS documentation to create, provided that the available documentation ensures effective planning, operation, and control of its processes. The number of system-level procedures specifically required is now reduced to only six as opposed to 18 in ISO 9001:1994 (refer to Table 2.1 for the list of required procedures). Note that it is acceptable if an organization chooses to combine some of the aforementioned procedures, for example, corrective action and preventive action. Clause 4.2 of ISO 9001:2000 contains specific documentation requirements, which are explained later in chapter 4.

☞   It is very important that quality professionals who have worked with the old ISO 9001:1994 standard adjust to the revised documentation requirements in ISO 9001:2000. Unfortunately, quality professionals accustomed to asking for numerous documented procedures (as per ISO 9001:1994) continue to operate in the same fashion in the ISO 9001:2000 era. Rather than asking the question whether the new procedure is really needed, often the rationale that the quality professional provides is: "If we don't document this procedure, we will have a finding in our ISO audit because the auditor will ask why this process is not documented." Such reasoning is flawed and perpetuates the myth that ISO 9000 requires that each QMS process be fully documented down to the last detail. Therefore,

Table 2.1 Overview of ISO 9001:2000 requirements.

ISO 9001:2000 Clause	Key Activities	Required Procedures	Required Records
4 Quality Management System			
4.1 General requirements	Identify processes in the QMS, including their sequence and interaction. Effectively implement and continually improve these processes.		
4.2 Documentation requirements	The following must be documented: quality policy, quality objectives, quality manual, procedures and records required by ISO 9001:2000, and procedures required by the organization. QMS documentation and records must be controlled.	• Control of documents procedure (subclause 4.2.3) • Control of records procedure (subclause 4.2.4)	
5 Management Responsibility			
5.1 Management commitment	Management must establish the quality policy and quality objectives, conduct management reviews, provide resources, and communicate to employees the importance of meeting customer and regulatory requirements.		
5.2 Customer focus	Management must ensure that all customer requirements are determined and satisfied.		
5.3 Quality policy	The quality policy must be relevant to the organization and must be founded on continual improvement. The quality policy must be communicated to all employees, and it must be reviewed periodically for appropriateness.		

Continued

ISO 9001:2000 Clause	Key Activities	Required Procedures	Required Records
5.4 Planning	Management must establish measurable quality objectives that are consistent with the quality policy. Management must ensure that planning processes are in place to meet the QMS requirements. In case of QMS changes, integrity of the system must be maintained.		
5.5 Responsibility, authority, and communication	Management must ensure that responsibilities are clearly defined and understood throughout the organization. Management must appoint a management representative who is ultimately responsible for the definition, deployment, and continual improvement of the QMS. Management must ensure that the effectiveness of the QMS is internally communicated to all employees.		
5.6 Management review	Management must conduct ongoing management review of the QMS to monitor effectiveness and identify opportunities for improvement.		• Management review records (subclause 5.6.1)
6 Resource Management			
6.1 Provision of resources	Resources needed for the establishment and continual improvement of the QMS must be provided.		
6.2 Human resources	It must be ensured that employees are qualified to do their job. Training needs for all employees must be identified and fulfilled. Adequate work environment and tools must be provided to the employees to perform their job effectively.		• Employee education, skills, experience, and training records (subclause 6.2.2)

Continued

ISO 9001:2000 Clause	Key Activities	Required Procedures	Required Records
7 Product Realization			
7.1 Planning of product realization	Product realization processes must be planned and established. These processes must be adequate for meeting product and customer requirements.		• Evidence that process and product requirements are met
7.2 Customer-related processes	All high-level product requirements must be adequately identified. Prior to a contractual agreement with the customer(s), the requirements must be reviewed for correctness, completeness, and feasibility. The organization must implement effective mechanisms for communicating with its customers.		• Contract and high-level requirements review records, including results of action items (subclause 7.2.2)
7.3 Design and development	All design and development activities must be planned and controlled. Detailed product requirements must be identified and reviewed. During design and development phases, the work performed must be reviewed. The final outputs must be verified against the requirements for the respective phase, and validated against the operational requirements. Changes during design and development must be controlled. This includes review and approval of changes prior to implementation and verification and validation after implementation.		• Detailed requirements and review records (subclause 7.3.2) • Design and development review records (subclause 7.3.4) • Design and development verification records (subclause 7.3.5) • Design and development validation records (subclause 7.3.6) • Records of review and approval of design and development changes (subclause 7.3.7)
7.4 Purchasing	Criteria for supplier evaluation and selection must be established and adhered to. Purchase requirements communicated to the supplier must clearly describe the purchased product. The purchased product, once received, must be verified against the specified requirements.		• Supplier evaluation records (if applicable) (subclause 7.4.1)

Continued

ISO 9001:2000 Clause	Key Activities	Required Procedures	Required Records
7.5 Production and service provision	Production and service processes must be executed under controlled conditions. Those production and service processes that may result in deficiencies after product or service delivery must be validated in advance. As appropriate, the product must be identifiable and traceable throughout the product realization process. Customer-supplied product or equipment for use during the product realization process must be identified, verified, and protected. The product must be properly handled during and after product realization, until delivery to the customer.		• Records of process validation (as required) (subclause 7.5.2) • Product traceability records (subclause 7.5.3) • Record of any customer property lost, damaged, or unfit for use (subclause 7.5.4)
7.6 Control of monitoring and measuring devices	Monitoring and measurement to be performed on the product must be determined along with required equipment. When required, the measuring equipment must be calibrated, the calibration status recorded, and the equipment protected from abuse.		• Record of calibration standard used (if no international/national standard exists) • Records of validity of measurements taken with uncalibrated equipment • Calibration and verification records
8 Measurement, analysis and improvement			
8.1 General	Processes for monitoring, measurement, analysis, and improvement of the product and the QMS must be established.		

Continued

Continued

ISO 9001:2000 Clause	Key Activities	Required Procedures	Required Records
8.2 Monitoring and measurement	Customer satisfaction data must be collected and used for continual improvement of the QMS. An internal audit program must be established. Audits must be planned, impartial, and followed up to verify the corrective and/or preventive actions taken. QMS processes must be monitored and measured, as appropriate, to ensure they meet their intended objective(s). The product must be monitored and measured to verify conformance to acceptance criteria.	• Internal audits procedure (subclause 8.2.2)	• Internal audit results and follow-up records (subclause 8.2.2) • Record of person(s) authorizing release of product (subclause 8.2.4)
8.3 Control of nonconforming product	Nonconforming product must be controlled to preclude its delivery to and use by the customer (unless authorized otherwise by the customer or a relevant authority). When appropriate, it must be corrected and reverified prior to delivery to the customer.	• Control of nonconforming product procedure	• Records of product nonconformance and of subsequent follow-up
8.4 Analysis of data	Measurement data must be analyzed to verify effectiveness of the QMS, and to identify opportunities for improvement.		
8.5 Improvement	The QMS must be continually improved by using the quality policy, quality objectives, internal audits, measurement data analysis, management review, and corrective and preventive action. All known nonconformities must be eliminated by taking appropriate corrective action, and potential nonconformities must be eliminated by taking appropriate preventive action.	• Corrective action procedure (subclause 8.5.2) • Preventive action procedure (subclause 8.5.3)	• Results of corrective action (subclause 8.5.2) • Results of preventive action (subclause 8.5.3)

prior to documenting a process, the need to document it and the extent to which it should be documented should be carefully assessed against the criteria listed in subclause 4.2.1 of ISO 9001:2000.

ISO 9001:2000 CONTENT OVERVIEW

The previous section provided an overview of how ISO 9001:2000 requirements are grouped into five major clauses. This section will serve as a quick reference to the key activities that need to be implemented to comply with each requirement (refer to Table 2.1). Mandatory procedures and records that need to be established are also identified. Detailed discussion on each requirement is deferred to chapters 4 through 8.

RELEVANCE OF ISO 90003 TO SOFTWARE DEVELOPMENT ORGANIZATIONS

Because this book is written to provide ISO 9001:2000 implementation guidance for the software industry, this chapter would not be complete without a brief introduction to ISO 90003.[1] ISO 90003 is the official guideline document released by ISO that provides guidance on the application of ISO 9001:2000 to the specification, design, development, test, and maintenance of software, including acquisition of third-party software. It is important to note that unlike ISO 9001:2000, an organization cannot be registered to ISO 90003. However, ISO 90003 is intended to be used as a reference document to understand what each ISO 9001:2000 requirement means in the context of the software industry.

While writing this book, ISO 90003 has been used as a reference, and all implementation guidance included in later chapters is consistent with and builds upon the interpretation included in ISO 90003. Throughout ISO 90003, references are provided to additional ISO guideline documents for the software industry, the use of which is optional. In other words, these guideline documents are not intended to prescribe how you must comply with the associated ISO 9001:2000 requirements. In fact, if a software development company has an approach that adequately meets the ISO requirement, it is perfectly acceptable even if the approach is different from the one stated in an ISO guideline document referenced in ISO 90003. For this reason, and in order to avoid redundancy, such ISO guideline documents referenced in ISO 90003 are not listed in this book (please refer to your official copy of ISO 90003).*

Finally, a word about ISO 12207, which is perhaps the most frequently cited reference in ISO 90003. ISO 12207 provides a framework (or architecture) for software lifecycle processes, activities, and tasks. The scope of this standard covers processes for software acquisition, software supply, software development, operations, and maintenance. Because ISO 9001:2000 emphasizes a process-based approach to quality management, ISO 12207 is a natural complement to ISO 90003 for the software industry. Organizations may use ISO 12207 as a reference while defining the architecture and linkages of their software lifecycle processes because it provides guidance on what processes should be implemented and what activities and tasks they should contain, although it does not prescribe how to perform the activities and tasks. It is also important to recognize what ISO 12207 is not. Unlike ISO 9001:2000, ISO 12207 is *not* a quality standard to which registration can be obtained. Also, unlike ISO 90003, ISO 12207 does *not* offer interpretation advice on ISO 9001:2000 for the software industry. ISO 90003 points out that ISO 12207 *may* be used for additional guidance and to *complement* processes established in accordance with ISO 9001:2000 requirements. As stated earlier, use of ISO 12207 is optional, and therefore, discussion on it is beyond the scope of this book.

ENDNOTE

1. All references to ISO 90003 in this book refer to the revised version of the standard, which is titled *Software and System Engineering—Guidelines for the Application of ISO 9001:2000 to Computer Software* (ISO FDIS 90003). This new version of ISO 90003 supersedes the previous version released in the year 1997 (ISO 9000-3:1997).

---

* It is recommended, but not necessary, that you procure an official copy of ISO 90003. However, this book was written with the assumption that the reader may *not* have a copy of ISO 90003. Therefore, not having an official copy of ISO 90003 will not impede your ability to follow the guidance in this book to implement an ISO 9001:2000–compliant QMS.

3

Implementation Strategy

Having gained a good understanding of what ISO 9000 is and what it entails, you are now ready to begin your QMS implementation . . . or are you? What are the essential prerequisites that must be met in order to ensure that your implementation proceeds as planned? How should you approach your QMS implementation? Who should implement the QMS? What costs and time duration are involved? What tools can you use to monitor your implementation and keep it on track at all times? What are the pitfalls to avoid? These are some of the pertinent questions related to ISO 9000 implementation that are answered in this chapter. This chapter also provides guidance on how ISO 9001:2000 requirements may be applied to any organization, regardless of the organization's type, size, and product. This chapter concludes with a recommended process for successful implementation of an ISO 9000–based QMS.

THE ISO 9001:2000
IMPLEMENTATION PROJECT

In order to achieve ISO 9000 registration within the allocated budget and time, and for the implemented QMS to be truly deployed and adhered to, there are three essential prerequisites that must be met. These are described in the next section in decreasing order of priority. Subsequent sections provide detailed guidance on how to plan and manage an ISO 9000 implementation project.

Prerequisites for a Successful Implementation

1. *Management commitment.* First and foremost, senior management's commitment to quality and to implementing a QMS in accordance with ISO 9001:2000 requirements must be established (as per clause 5.1). Quite often, organizations fail in their effort to establish a QMS primarily due to lack of senior management commitment and support. Management's commitment to quality does not end with the organization succeeding in achieving ISO 9000 registration. Sustained senior management commitment *beyond* ISO 9000 registration is essential for an organization to continuously improve itself. This is because an ISO 9000 registration does not and should not signify the ultimate goal of an organization's quality improvement effort. On the contrary, ISO 9000 registration means that your organization has successfully established a sound infrastructure for quality management and improvement, which will enable your company to continuously improve in the future. An ISO 9000–registered organization has quality practices and tools in place that it can use to be a quality-driven company. Therefore, in order to reap all the long-term rewards of ISO 9000 registration, continued management support for the QMS is vital.

2. *Management representative.* The second prerequisite is that senior management must identify a member of management who will serve as the management representative (as per subclause 5.5.2). The management representative is ultimately responsible for the definition, deployment, monitoring, and continuous improvement of the organization's ISO 9000–compliant QMS. During ISO 9000 implementation, the management representative directs and guides the ISO 9000 implementation team on a daily basis, while after ISO 9000 implementation the responsibility pertains to maintenance and continuous improvement of the QMS. It is highly recommended that the organization choose its quality officer[1] as its management representative instead of assigning this role to a management person from some other functional area (ISO 9001:2000 does not preclude an organization from doing so). This is because an implementation team is generally best served by a "hands-on" management representative who has the necessary experience and skills to effectively participate in the implementation, deployment, and continuous improvement of the QMS.

The management representative will be frequently answering questions such as:

- Why does the organization need a QMS?

- What is the scope of a business process?

- Which organizations interface during a process and what are their interfaces?

- What are the bottlenecks and areas for improvement in a process?

- How should a process be documented and who should document it?

- How much documentation is adequate for a process?

- Will a proposed process work or not? Why or why not?

- What type of controls should be included in a process to ensure it performs as desired?

- What are the right measurements for monitoring quality?

- What is the root cause for a process or quality problem?

- What is the most appropriate corrective or preventive action for an observed quality problem?

As is evident, not having the right person in this role can significantly hurt an organization's chances of implementing a QMS that is adequate, effective, not unnecessarily complex, and implemented in a timely fashion. There are certain desirable traits of an ideal management representative:

• He or she has a sound understanding of and recognized expertise in most phases of the software development and maintenance process—beginning with requirements definition and contractual negotiations, and ending with supporting customers after product release. This experience may have been obtained in a direct capacity by working in various roles in the software industry, or in an indirect capacity from having worked intimately and extensively with personnel in various roles in the software industry. It is critically important that the person be of *recognized expertise*, that is, the person be widely respected in the organization on the basis of the person's genuine breadth and depth of knowledge and experience.

• The management representative should have prior experience in implementing quality management systems in software development organizations, either using ISO 9000 or other quality standards.

• The management representative should be capable of taking a *system-level* view of the implementation in order to explain to employees how all the business processes interact to ultimately deliver a quality product.

• The management representative should be biased toward requiring only as much documentation as is necessary to ensure the effective planning, execution, control, and improvement of processes. A QMS that consists of a complex maze of process documentation is against the spirit of ISO 9000 and will in fact reduce process efficiency. It has also been observed that often organizations get bogged down in trying to implement "the perfect QMS" as opposed to implementing a system that is functional, complies with ISO 9001:2000 requirements, and can be gradually improved over time. Therefore, it is imperative that the management representative adopt a pragmatic yet sound approach to implementing the QMS. After all, quality improvements due to their very nature are usually achieved incrementally— by learning from past mistakes, successes, and experiences. Therefore, to expend an enormous amount of effort up front in trying to implement the perfect system is futile and may result in an unnecessarily complex QMS.

• The management representative should possess strong project management skills and should be capable of coordinating and monitoring daily progress of the implementation team.

• Last but not least, the management representative should have excellent soft skills—this includes sound people management skills; ability to effectively represent the organization in meetings with customers and third parties on quality issues; ability to manage expectations of all employees (management personnel and staff); ability to influence and be persuasive as a champion of quality; and ability to work with people in a nonconfrontational and cooperative manner. It should be recognized that the management representative is meant to be the organization's foremost *agent of change*. Therefore, an individual who exhibits personality traits of being argumentative, stubborn, and generally nonreceptive to other people's ideas is antithetical to what this role requires.

3. *Implementation planning.* The third and final prerequisite is detailed implementation planning, and establishment of mechanisms for tracking and controlling the QMS implementation (as per subclause 5.4.2). Lack of sufficient planning is likely to result in numerous problems during implementation, such as inconsistencies in the implemented QMS, inadequate or excessive process documentation, incorrect documentation, schedule delays, repeated rework, poor deployment of the system, and poor employee awareness of the QMS. Therefore, in order to preclude such problems, the organization must decide beforehand how to approach the ISO 9000 implementation, how to track the implementation progress, and what mechanisms to use to keep the implementation progress on track. Detailed guidance on how to plan, track, and control an ISO 9000 implementation is provided in subsequent sections of this chapter.

Planning the Implementation

All projects executed in organizations share some common characteristics. Each project entails an implementation team working toward a defined project goal, with an allocated budget, defined time schedule, and provided resources. Project success is determined by how well the implementation team achieved the project goal, how effectively the provided resources were utilized, and whether the project goal was achieved within the allocated budget and time. It is important to realize that an ISO 9000 implementation also shares all of these characteristics. Therefore, when an organization embarks on its ISO 9000 implementation, it is best to approach the implementation as a *project*. What does this mean? It means that similar to any other project, an ISO 9000 implementation should also be planned, tracked, and controlled with the same degree of formality and diligence. In order to perform these three tasks effectively, a project plan must first be prepared. The project plan describes the goal of the project team and how the team plans to achieve it. The purpose of such a document is primarily to stimulate adequate amount of diligent thinking and preparation by the implementation team before proceeding with the implementation. As we know, a well-planned implementation approach for a project will certainly increase the likelihood of the project progressing smoothly, and help minimize any wastage of resources in reworking flawed implementation. Following is the type of information that the project plan should address:

Project Goal

The project goal should be defined by senior management and it should meet the SMART[2] criteria (specific, measurable, acceptable, realistic, time-bound):

• A *specific* goal is one that clearly states the final objective and its scope. For example, "Achieve ISO 9000" would not be a specific goal, as it is unclear what the scope of the ISO 9000 implementation is. Does the ISO 9000 implementation encompass all the products and locations of the organization? Does the implementation include design, development, production, installation, and servicing of the product(s)?

• A goal is *measurable* if it is clear to the reader how the attainment of the goal will be validated. For example, "Achieve ISO 9000 for the design, development, production, installation, and servicing of all products of ABC Corporation" would be a specific but nonmeasurable goal. This is because it is unclear how the achievement of this goal will be demonstrated. Specifically, does the organization intend to self-declare compliance or attain formal registration to ISO 9000?

- A goal is *acceptable* if it is agreeable to the implementation team. If a project's goal has been foisted on a reluctant implementation team, then the project is doomed to failure.

- A goal is *realistic* if it is achievable within the identified time frame. A goal that is overly ambitious at the outset is bound to have little or no likelihood of being achieved. For example, if an organization with 500 employees were implementing a QMS from scratch, a goal of attaining registration in six months would be nearly impossible.

- Finally, a goal is *time-bound* if it clearly states by when the goal is intended to be achieved. Therefore, keeping in mind the aforementioned criteria, a SMART goal would be "To achieve ISO 9000 registration by October 19, 2003, for all activities pertaining to the design, development, production, installation, and servicing of *X* product at all company sites of ABC Corporation." This, of course, assumes that the goal is realistic and agreed to by the implementation team.

☞ In order to maximize the chances for the achievement of the stated project goal it is recommended that the achievement of the project goal, and of the intermediate milestones, be tied to annual employee objectives as part of the employee performance appraisal process for all employees. Because this in turn affects the bonus/reward disbursement to employees, it serves as an excellent incentive to facilitate the achievement of the identified milestones and final project goal.

Implementation Team

Once a clear project goal has been defined, the organization should establish an ISO 9000 implementation team. ISO 9000 implementation is best accomplished by involving all the departments and practitioners in a *participative* fashion as opposed to the QMS being defined by a "quality expert" in isolation. Cross-functional participation in process definitions and reviews helps secure the buy-in of the various stakeholders and reduces resistance to change in the deployment phase. This is because, by participating in the definition of the QMS processes as opposed to being dictated to follow a specific process, employees are provided an opportunity to review the QMS and offer constructive criticism during its definition. QMS documentation that is built on consensus fosters a sense of ownership and commitment to the defined system, which is essential for the acceptance and deployment of the defined system. Bear in mind that every department and its employees possess a high degree of pride of ownership and expertise in their respective processes. Therefore, quite reasonably, they find it hard to accept a QMS that was defined without soliciting their input. After all, how good is a process definition if it was documented without soliciting the input of the practitioners who execute that process? A QMS defined in such a fashion is viewed by the employees as having been foisted upon them, thus increasing the odds against its widespread acceptance and use. Therefore, in order to participate in the ISO 9000 implementation effort, each department should identify an employee, who we can call the process improvement group member (PGM), to represent the department as a member of the ISO 9000 implementation team.[3]

The ISO 9000 implementation team is led by the organization's management representative, assisted by the quality department (if one exists).

☞ It is recognized that all organizations may not have a separate quality department, nor is one specifically required by ISO 9001:2000. For example, a small organization may only have one person fulfilling such a role, while another small organization may have an informal quality organization, similar to a software engineering process group (SEPG), but comprising personnel assigned part-time. Throughout this book, the term "quality department" refers to the *quality function* in the organization, regardless of how it is staffed and structured. Note that the quality department should not be confused with the product test department, although many organizations continue to incorrectly label their product test department as the quality department. The quality department primarily includes process engineers to perform *independent* quality assurance and control. In order to be unbiased and free from influence, personnel in the quality function should minimally have organizational freedom and authority from persons participating in the software product development process (SPDP), and preferably, from persons participating in the meta-process as well. (Meta-process and SPDP are explained later in this chapter.)

When a dedicated quality department exists, it is a constant entity within the organization, even after implementation of the system and registration of the organization to ISO 9000. This is because, beyond registration, the quality department is involved in auditing the QMS, continuous improvement of the QMS, reporting to management on the ongoing state of the QMS, facilitating audits by customers, and facilitating periodic ISO 9000 surveillance audits by the registrar for the continuing validity of the registration.

Consider the organization chart of a software development organization shown in Figure 3.1,[4] where the shaded departments are within the scope of the organization's ISO 9000 registration. In this example, PGMs should represent each of the shaded departments as members of the ISO 9000 implementation team.

The PGM should ideally be an employee who has been with the organization for a sufficient amount of time, such that he or she is knowledgeable

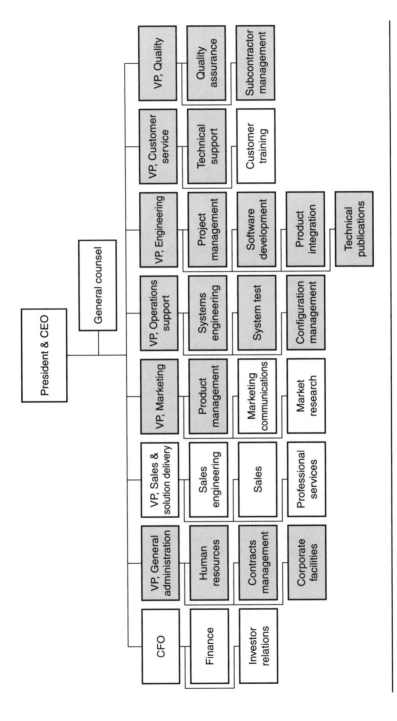

Figure 3.1 Organization chart of a software development organization.

in the department's processes and in other cross-functional processes that involve the department. It is also highly desirable that the PGM have extensive and varied prior industry experience in the respective functional area. The PGM should have good oral and written communication skills. The PGM should be recognized in the organization as a person who is committed to quality, and the quality department should be confident that the proposed PGM would be a valuable contribution to the implementation team. It is desirable that prior to selecting the PGM for the department, the department supervisor should contact the quality department regarding the proposed person and work with the quality department to pick the most suitable candidate. It is also important to keep in mind that the candidate should not be one who is regarded as the most critical employee of the department and who already has an excessive workload. An ISO 9000 implementation requires a significant amount of effort from the implementation team; therefore, lack of sufficient participation by a department can significantly affect the ISO 9000 implementation progress in the respective department.

The PGM participates on an as-needed basis in all activities and meetings pertaining to the ISO 9000 implementation. In the case of large organizations, the chosen PGM may also represent all the subdepartments within that department, and therefore, separate PGMs for each of the subdepartments may not be required. Responsibilities for PGMs may include but are not limited to:

- Serving as the single point of contact between the quality department and the PGM's department for all issues pertaining to the ISO 9000 implementation (including participation in implementation planning, and championing QMS implementation in the department).

- Participating in the identification of business processes in which the PGM's department is involved.

- Producing QMS documentation assigned to the PGM by the implementation team. The PGM may also delegate generation of some QMS documentation to other individuals in his or her department, but he or she is ultimately responsible for the assigned task being completed as per the agreed dates.

- Ensuring that interfaces with other processes and departments have been addressed in the QMS documentation and the documentation has been reviewed with the interfacing departments. This is necessary to ensure that the documentation is correct and complete (process verification).

- Ensuring that all ISO 9001:2000 requirements applicable to the process have been satisfactorily addressed (process validation).

- Participating in the review of cross-functional process definitions (that is, process definitions spanning multiple departments).

- Providing process training or assisting the quality department to provide process training to employees on processes owned by the PGM's department.

- Implementing corrective and preventive actions (as required) after quality audits and assessments.

Guidance on how the management representative should work with the PGMs and how to achieve desirable results from the PGMs is provided later in this chapter.

Cost of Registration

Prior to beginning detailed project planning, the quality department must be familiar with the cost and effort associated with an ISO 9000 registration. This will enable better plans to be laid out in terms of needed resources, project budget, and expected time duration. As needed, for administrative purposes, the organization may establish mechanisms to monitor actual costs during ISO 9000 implementation.

There are primarily two types of costs involved with an ISO 9000 registration:

1. *Costs associated with implementing ISO 9000.* These include personnel costs (both budgeted and nonbudgeted), and costs pertaining to needed tools, training, travel, resources, consultancy, and other miscellaneous expenses. If a quality department is nonexistent or understaffed, then the management representative will need to first budget for and secure the funding to adequately staff the quality department. Because a PGM is merely a role assigned to an existing employee, there are no special costs that need to be budgeted for PGMs. That is, a certain amount of money does not need to be set aside for hiring of PGMs. However, effort required from PGMs should be estimated so that management can determine and plan for its expected impact on the regular job responsibilities of the PGMs. Effort required from other personnel should also be planned for, such as department managers who may be invited to reviews of QMS documents pertinent to their work.

When ISO 9000 training is provided by an outside vendor, costs should be budgeted for first-time and ongoing ISO 9000 training for all employees in the organization (including training of the ISO 9000 implementation team). If the personnel in the quality department are not already qualified as quality auditors, then costs should be budgeted for internal quality auditor training for the personnel, including lead auditor training for some personnel. Costs should also be budgeted for the purchase of ISO 9000–related books and sufficient official copies of the standard.

In case of multisite organizations, a significant amount of cost is associated with travel between sites to ensure inter-site coordination and consistency in QMS implementation, and such travel costs should be budgeted. Costs associated with procurement of any needed hardware and software tools, such as commercial software tools for creation of quality procedures and electronic implementation of the QMS, should also be budgeted.

If the organization intends to attend networking meetings with quality personnel at the local chapter of the ASQ or similar organizations, then budget must be allocated for travel and attendance at such meetings. Consideration should also be given to professional quality membership-related costs. If the organization plans to sponsor industry quality events, then suitable funds must be allocated for that purpose. If the organization intends to engage an outside consultant to help in the implementation of its QMS, then it must allocate sufficient funds for it.

Finally, there must be some funds budgeted for employee rewards and recognition, such as small gifts to recognize employee contributions, meals to celebrate milestones, and quality merchandise for distribution to employees, for example, quality mugs or t-shirts stating the organizational quality policy.

2. *Costs associated with the ISO 9000 registration process.* These are the costs associated with the registration process itself. Therefore, these costs come into play once an organization has implemented its QMS and is ready to engage a registrar who will perform the ISO 9000 registration audit. The registration cost is different for each organization and depends on a variety of factors, such as:

- Size of the organization (has a bearing on audit days)

- Scope of the registration (has a bearing on audit days)

- Number of company locations to be registered (has a bearing on the extent, and thus cost, of the preassessment audit)

- Level of maturity of the organization's QMS (has a bearing on the extent, and thus cost, of the preassessment audit)

- Number of audit findings that need to be addressed prior to registration (has a bearing on the duration and number of corrective action follow-ups, which in turn has a bearing on the cost of the follow-ups)

The registration costs quoted by the registrars are open to negotiation prior to contractual agreement, and therefore the quoted costs should be negotiated. From personal experience, for the same registration parameters, the price quotes by different registrars have been known to show a variance of about 10 percent to 15 percent, but instances have also been observed where some registrars quote a price that is as much as 30 percent higher than the average quote. This illustrates that it is always in the best interest of the organization to engage in registrar selection discussions with multiple registrars as opposed to talking to only one. Other benefits of considering multiple registrars are discussed in chapter 9. Table 3.1 provides an example of the types of ISO 9000 registration costs that are typically quoted by a registrar. Be aware that for those organizations that do not wish to deal with the unknowns associated with the "additional costs" listed in Table 3.1, some registrars also provide the option of a fixed daily rate that is all-inclusive but obviously higher than the daily rate that they would charge exclusive of such expenses. Such all-inclusive daily rates continue

Table 3.1 Sample ISO 9000 registration costs (for a three-year registration period) quoted by a registrar for a 300-employee single-site registration.

Registration Cost	Daily Rate	Number of Man Days	Cost
Fixed Costs			
Gap analysis (optional)	$1300	1	$1300
Preassessment (optional)	$1300	4	$5200
Documentation audit	$1300	2	$2600
Registration audit planning	$1300	2	$2600
Registration audit	$1300	10	$13,000
Registration fee	–	–	$500
Publicity material (banners, posters, and so on)	–	–	$500
Surveillance audit planning (five surveillance audits @ six month frequency for three-year period)	$1300	5	$6500
Surveillance audits	$1300	10	$13,000
Total Fixed Cost:			$45,200
Additional Costs (Charged on Actual Basis):			
Travel time	$80/hour of travel	Actual	$80 × travel time in hours
Major nonconformance follow-up visit	$175/hour	Actual	$175 × hours
Other expenses: airfare, accommodation, food, and car rental	–	–	Actual expense

to be less prevalent though, because the registrars, upon request, can usually provide a rough estimate of the total expenses to expect in the "additional costs" category.

Time Frame for Achieving Registration

As far as the overall time frame for achieving ISO 9000 registration is concerned, it is not possible to define one time frame that would apply equally well to all organizations. This is because just as the cost of the implementation is dependent on various factors and varies with each organization, the time frame for implementation is dictated by various factors and is unique to each organization. The factors that have a bearing on registration cost also affect implementation time frame. Some additional factors are:

- Degree of management commitment to implementing a QMS

- Amount of documentation that needs to be defined, reviewed, and approved to meet ISO 9000 requirements

- Amount of QMS training that needs to be imparted to the employees

- Amount of time required for process establishment throughout the organization (process establishment is explained later in this chapter)

- Number of internal quality audits that are anticipated to verify complete deployment and use of the defined QMS

- Number and nature of corrective and preventive actions to be implemented as a result of the internal quality audits

Even though the exact time frame is unique to each organization, typical estimates of ISO 9000 implementation time frames are available, and these can be used as a guideline by any organization pursuing an ISO 9000 registration. Assuming that the senior management of an organization is totally committed to achieving ISO 9000 registration, Table 3.2 shows the typical estimated duration to achieve ISO 9000 registration for a medium-sized organization (at least 100 employees) with an adequately staffed quality department. In the case of organizations to which the concept of a QMS is totally alien or relatively new, a substantially longer time for implementation of a QMS should be expected. The fundamental reason for this is not merely the fact that there is a lot of work that needs to be done, but because a substantial amount of time is needed to overcome resistance to change and affect a change in organizational culture. To have an organization rethink how it operates and have its processes embody quality practices is

Table 3.2 Estimated time frames for achieving ISO 9000 registration in a medium-size organization.

State of the Organization's QMS	Expected Duration for ISO 9000 Registration
Negligible effort has been expended in implementing quality practices. Processes, procedures, and records are practically nonexistent.	18–24 months
Some effort has been expended in implementing quality practices. A few processes, procedures, and records exist.	12–18 months
A reasonably well-defined QMS exists. Key processes have been documented and key records are maintained.	6–12 months
A well-defined QMS exists. The QMS is internally audited. The QMS may currently be registered to some other quality standard.	Up to 6 months

not trivial. If an organization's employees have been accustomed to working in a certain way, they are bound to question any new requirements placed on them. The onus is on the management representative and the quality department to champion the QMS implementation, and facilitate the transition of the employees from the old way of working to the new and improved way of working.

Tracking and Control

We know that a plan is only as good as its implementation. To ensure faithful execution of an implementation plan, it is crucial that the implementation team have mechanisms to track implementation progress, manage ongoing implementation issues and risks, and take timely corrective action in case execution deviates from plans. In order to perform effective implementation tracking and oversight, the following simple tools have been found to be very effective.

QMS Documents—Status Sheet

A simple sheet that lists due dates and current status of each of the QMS documents being created is essential for tracking detailed progress status. Because an ISO 9000 implementation entails the creation of a number of QMS documents, it is imperative that the implementation team, at any time, be able to quickly determine the status of each QMS document being created. This helps the implementation team not only monitor if the authors of the QMS documents are adhering to the due dates, but it also enables the team to provide status upon request by management and other employees.

It is recommended that this list be maintained by the quality department, be updated daily, and be stored in a location that is easily accessible to all employees (including senior management).

QMS Implementation—Actions Items and Risks Log

In addition to the QMS Documents–Status Sheet, another essential status tracking tool is an ongoing action items and risks log. Each of the ISO 9000 implementation activities entails the execution of a number of detailed day-to-day implementation tasks, and assignment of related action items and monitoring of risks. While the respective PGMs have the responsibility for identifying, coordinating, and tracking the tasks that pertain to their processes and departments, the quality department has a similar responsibility for identifying, coordinating, and tracking tasks that are the responsibility of the quality department, or pertain to interdepartmental issues. Therefore, such a log is used to perform day-to-day management and it serves as a short-term work plan with tasks being identified and planned for on a daily or weekly basis. The quality department personnel should collectively review the QMS Documents—Status Sheet and QMS Implementation-Actions Items and Risks Log, preferably on a daily basis, and minimally on a weekly basis. This enables the quality department to ensure tight control of project execution and facilitates timely identification and addressing of project risks. It enables the quality department to discuss any slippages in department progress with the responsible PGMs, failing which any issues can be escalated to the periodic senior management reviews (see "Status Reporting to Senior Management," page 43).

Communications

Effective communication is a critical element of a successful ISO 9000 implementation. It ensures that the ISO 9000 implementation team shares a common understanding of what needs to be achieved, and is consistent in its implementation approach. Communication is also needed to keep management personnel informed about implementation status and issues requiring their intervention. Employee communication is required during ISO 9000 implementation to keep employees informed regarding the changes being rolled out and the impact on them, and to keep them motivated toward the goal by reporting on successes achieved. In fact, such communication is not only required during ISO 9000 implementation, but also beyond that (refer to subclause 5.5.3). Having listed some of the reasons for the need for communication mechanisms, let's look at some of the communication vehicles an organization may use, not only during the course of its ISO 9000 implementation, but also beyond that.

Communication with PGMs

As discussed earlier in this chapter, PGMs are a vital interface between the quality department and the various departments in an organization. Therefore, constant communication with them is vital. Periodic meetings should be held with the PGMs during and after ISO 9000 implementation. These include meetings for: reviewing QMS documents with the relevant PGMs and department personnel (prior to document approval), and coordination meetings with the PGMs to discuss activities to be performed for development and continuous improvement of the QMS. Such coordination meetings enable the quality department to propagate its message and plans to the respective departments via the PGMs. Such meetings also serve as a forum for free exchange of ideas between the quality department and the PGMs, and enable the quality department to lay down priorities and emphasize constancy of purpose to the PGMs and their respective departments.

Communication with All Employees

In addition to communication meetings with the PGMs, it is also important for the success of the ISO 9000 implementation effort that senior management and the quality department communicate directly with all employees. For this purpose, senior management should at "all-hands" and staff meetings emphasize the importance of quality and continuous improvement. Note that ISO 9001:2000 contains specific requirements pertaining to employee communication in clause 5.1, and subclause 5.5.3.

For the purpose of employee communication, strategically located bulletin boards and posters can also be very useful. Bulletin boards can be used to display information that is pertinent to the ISO 9000 implementation phase in progress. For example, during implementation, the displayed information may include a list of the QMS documents that have been created in each department, while closer to the registration audit, the posted information may inform the employees of the audit schedule and what to expect in the audits. Care should be taken to keep the bulletin boards and posters brief yet sufficiently attractive, so that a passerby would be tempted to stop and read the material. Displaying excess information is counterproductive and likely to discourage the employee from reading the posted information.

In addition to the aforementioned items, periodic newsletters (preferably sent by e-mail) can be an effective means of communicating with all employees. Such newsletters should be brief, say one page or less, and not sent so frequently as to cause the employee to regard it as junk mail and discard it without reading. Depending on the overall time frame for implementation, a newsletter every two months, but no more than monthly, is usually sufficient. The newsletter should draw the attention of the employees to the accomplishments in the ISO 9000 implementation to date, what to expect in the coming days (until the next newsletter), and recognize employees (including PGMs) who have made significant contributions to the development of the QMS.

Another vehicle that may be used for internal communication is a quality Web site on the organization's intranet. This Web site may be used during ISO 9000 implementation to communicate departmental progress, including accomplishments and current and planned activities. The Web site may be used for soliciting improvement suggestions from employees and for providing information regarding corrective and preventive actions in implementation. In addition, the Web site may also be used to share process and product measurement information with employees (access may be restricted if required). Note that such a quality Web site is primarily meant to be for informational purposes only, and is separate from the controlled repository of QMS documentation, which may also be implemented electronically.

Other useful means of communicating with employees include sending out "quality alert" e-mails to appropriate departments regarding pertinent quality issues, for example, to clear misunderstandings regarding key elements of the QMS, to caution about observed discrepancies from the QMS, and to draw attention to key requirements of the QMS. Quick reference cards may also be distributed to succinctly summarize key elements of the QMS. Finally, quality contests and associated prizes also serve as an effective way to encourage employee participation in the QMS establishment effort. For example, employees may be quizzed on elements of the organization's QMS. Such contests help familiarize the employees with the QMS terminology and promote use of the QMS.

Status Reporting to Senior Management

As stated earlier, management commitment and continued active involvement in QMS development is the most important prerequisite to achieving ISO 9000 registration. In fact, regular management review of the QMS is one of the key requirements of the ISO 9000 standard. During ISO 9000 implementation, it is important that the quality department keep senior management informed regarding the implementation progress in all departments. For this purpose, the quality department should establish a scale and criteria to measure progress, and the methods used to measure progress should be communicated to all PGMs. For example, a sample scale and criteria are shown in Table 3.3.

PGMs should be made aware that detailed ISO 9000 progress status is reported at management reviews. Such status reporting to senior management helps ensure that all departments accord high priority to their respective tasks. It is useful from a senior management perspective to be provided an overall slide showing quantitative progress for each department (see

Table 3.3   Scale and criteria to measure ISO 9000 implementation progress.

Scale	Points	Criteria
0–20	20	Draft versions of all requested QMS documents have been produced, and they are ready for informal review by the quality department. For example, if four QMS documents are requested from the department, then you should consider each draft document to be worth five points.
21–40	20	All draft documents have been reworked after informal review, and are now ready for interdepartmental formal review.
41–60	20	All documents have been reworked and approved after formal review.
61–75	15	All employees in the department have been trained on applicable QMS documents.
76–90	15	Department has been audited by the quality department and it has responded with an acceptable corrective action plan.
91–100	10	Corrective action follow-up audit has been performed by the quality department and the department is now ready for the ISO 9000 registration audit.

Figure 3.2), along with one slide, per department, to report specific issues (see Figure 3.3). As an example, Figure 3.2 shows a high-level overview of the current status of ISO 9000 implementation in a company. All departments are awarded a *score* on a scale of zero to 100 (using the scale in Table 3.3). The figure shows the score for each department for the current month and for the previous month (the difference between the two is the *progress* made by the department since the previous month). As an example, the detailed status of a department, and the breakdown of its score for the current month, is shown in Figure 3.3.

The quality department should not spend an undue amount of time trying to arrive at the most accurate score for a department. This is not intended to be an exact science; it is only meant to serve as a high-level, yet reasonably accurate estimate of each department's progress. The quality department will need to exercise discretion while awarding points to account for progress from the last progress-reporting period. The importance of such progress reporting with measurement data, though sometimes painful to compute, should not be overlooked. From a management perspective, it provides a reasonably accurate status of each department's progress. Care should be taken to emphasize to senior management that progress percentages of their respective departments are systematically derived and are not arbitrary; at the same time, they are not intended to be accurate to the last digit. Therefore, it is important for them to keep this in perspective and not argue each individual score awarded by the quality department.

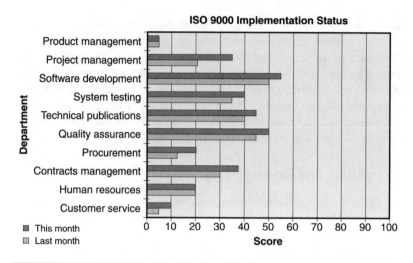

Figure 3.2 Overall ISO 9000 implementation status of some departments in an organization.

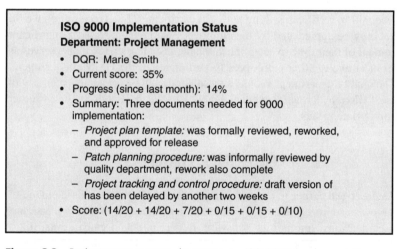

Figure 3.3 Project management department—ISO 9000 implementation status update.

External Communication and Networking

All the communication mechanisms discussed so far are for "internal communications," that is, for communications within the organization. If an organization were pursuing a prestigious quality standard certification, such as ISO 9000, then it certainly would be interested in knowing how other companies in its business domain achieved their registrations. Therefore, participation in an ISO 9000 network or users group can be very helpful for this purpose. Guidebooks such as this one serve as a useful source of information; however, it is always advantageous to network with other companies and benefit from their experiences. Moreover, networking in the industry also helps publicize an organization's quality improvement effort and draw attention of potential customers.

Recognition and Rewards

An ISO 9000 implementation requires time and commitment from all employees. Many employees will directly participate in the implementation effort by creating required QMS documents. Such efforts should be recognized by the quality department to thank the employees for their contribution and to ensure their continued support. Employee recognition can be made by means of a periodic newsletter, as described earlier. Individual contributors can also be recognized at company events or meetings by requesting senior management to hand out awards, such as employee recognition certificates along with gift certificates. Such recognition would not only be appreciated by the employees who have devoted a significant amount of their time to accomplish the requested tasks, but it also serves as an incentive to other employees to participate in the QMS establishment. The quality department should also celebrate milestone achievements with the PGMs by organizing team lunches on such occasions, or by other appropriate means.

GETTING STARTED

As described earlier in chapter 2, the revised ISO 9000 standard embodies a process approach. This is a welcome change because in recent years most organizations, including software development organizations, have embraced process management and improvement. The steady increase in the maturity levels of software development organizations, as reported by the Software Engineering Institute (SEI), which conducts process assessments against the well-known five-level Capability Maturity Model Integration (CMMI),[5] bear testimony to the growing acceptance of the process approach. The term "software process improvement," which was relatively new in the early 1990s, is now commonplace. Software literature now abounds with success stories and experience reports of companies on software process improvement. Indeed, software development organizations have learned and accepted to view quality, and the quest for it, though the lens of process management and improvement.

Therefore, it is only appropriate that before explaining the ISO 9000 requirements, an overview of a typical SPDP is provided. This will enable your organization to develop a shared understanding of the process for *product realization* in software development organizations. This process forms the essential context for all subsequent discussions in this book. This consistency in organizational understanding of the development process is key to fostering process and quality communication on the same plane.

Understanding the Software Development Lifecycle and Its Context

Before discussing the SPDP, it is beneficial to study the context in which this process is housed. That is, let's look at the "big picture" that constitutes the end-to-end process between the software development organization and its customer(s). The SPDP is only a constituent piece, although a very significant one, in this meta-process. Discussion on this meta-process is especially relevant because some of the requirements contained in ISO 9001:2000 pertain to this meta-process. As an example, requirements subclauses 7.2.1 and 7.2.2 pertain to customer requirements identification and review prior to contractual commitment (see Figure 3.4).

The Big Picture: The "Meta-Process"

An organization's meta-process is its end-to-end business process—beginning with the initial identification of a business opportunity with a current or prospective customer, and extending up to post-delivery support to the customer. Many organizations formally map this highest-level business process to promote internal communication on key business processes and their interfaces, and to assess bottlenecks and areas of improvements. Note that there are ancillary processes in this meta-process as well, such as financial processes, but it is the prerogative of the organization to decide the scope and depth of the meta-process map (in case it decides to create one). Be aware that creation of such a meta-process map is not mandated by ISO 9001:2000.

Following is a brief description of the major processes within the sample meta-process shown in Figure 3.4. Note that throughout this meta-process, organizations have some form of superordinate stop/go decision points for senior management review and decision based on the feasibility, risks, and benefits of a proposed new or enhanced product offering. Some of these superordinate decision points are depicted in Figure 3.4,

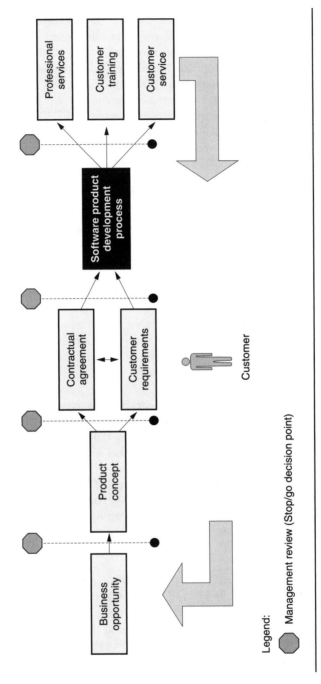

Figure 3.4   The meta-process map.

but organizations may define more of such decision points (including *within* the SPDP). Generally speaking, risks and uncertainties associated with the decision points are highest at the beginning and gradually decline as the meta-process progresses.

Business Opportunity. This process represents the initial identification of a potential business opportunity due to market research, customer input, or RFIs. The initial capture of a business opportunity is followed by preliminary senior management review to determine near-term and long-term revenue potential from pursuing the opportunity, and decision on whether to proceed with a detailed business case for the opportunity.

Product Concept. This process entails the high-level delineation of a proposed new product or key enhancements to a current product. This is followed by a detailed senior management review of the business case for the new product or product enhancement. Authorization to proceed is contingent upon an acceptable business case, and the proposed offering being in harmony with strategic direction for the product (in case of a product enhancement), and of the organization. This is, of course, assuming that the organization is a *product-based* organization and not a *contract-based* organization.

In the case of contract-based companies, the organization performs software development on contract, and the product is tailor-made to the customer's requirements. In the case of product-based companies, however, the product requirements are formulated by the organization by taking into consideration the needs of its current and potential customers. Therefore, the product requirements and its future evolution are the organization's prerogative and not contractually dictated by any one customer, although key customers may have a significant influence on the decisions. In such organizations, an internal road map for the evolution of the product exists that allocates product enhancements over future product releases. However, typically no one customer can dictate that all its requirements be implemented. For instance, the organization may reject customer requirements that are unique to one customer and are either financially nonviable or inconsistent with the organization's vision for the evolution of its product(s).

Customer Requirements. This process consists of eliciting specific product requirements from customers for implementation in futures releases. This process minimally culminates with the creation of a high-level specification of product requirements for the release. Generally, this process goes hand in hand with contractual negotiations with current or new customers who are interested in buying the new or enhanced product release. However, this may not always be the case. For example, in the case of software development companies developing commercial-off-the-shelf

(COTS) software, new releases for the software product are planned and released for sale in the general market.

The requirements at this stage are specified at a level that is adequate for communication and contractual negotiation with interested customers. In cases where firm commitment on a release date is required by a customer, a greater granularity in requirements specification is necessary at this stage, but seldom done. In most cases, software development projects commence with a predetermined release date and vague requirements. Subsequently, when the true scope of the effort becomes apparent, realization dawns that the release date is unrealistic. The search then begins to find ways to circumvent the problem. Unfortunately, this usually results in the scaling back, or complete elimination of, certain quality control and quality assurance activities, thus jeopardizing the quality of the product.[6] To preclude such a situation, when a release date is to be committed to, the organization should create a product requirements document (PRD), or a system specification, which then serves as the basis for negotiating a release date for the product (refer to Product Requirements Document Template in appendix B). Such a PRD is generally created by a system engineer or by the product manager.

Contractual Agreement. This process entails documenting the terms and conditions of the product sale in a legally binding agreement between the buyer and the seller. Prior to contract approval, the contract is jointly reviewed to ensure that the terms and conditions are mutually acceptable. This includes ensuring the requirements are clearly and unambiguously documented; confirmation by the seller that it has the capability to meet the stipulated requirements; and agreement on a mechanism for implementing future amendments to the contract (when needed).

Software Product Development Process (SPDP). This process embodies a systematic and disciplined approach to product realization in software development organizations. Because the SPDP is the foundation for most of the requirements explanation later, it is discussed separately in detail in the next subsection. This process is preceded by a senior management review that assesses whether the organization is ready to begin execution on a project. This entails determining whether documents that need to be available at this stage, as per the organization's business processes, are indeed available. This process ends with the availability of a product that can be made generally available (GA) to all customers. A project team meeting takes place at this point to assess the readiness of the product for release against predetermined criteria, and recommendation on product release is made to the appropriate personnel who have authority to release the product. The product is recommended for release if all the release criteria have been met. In the case of deviations from the criteria, the product may be recommended for release if the deviations are deemed acceptable, in that they do not jeopardize customer use, and associated risks have been mitigated.

Customer Training. This process entails implementation and maintenance of a customer training program. The training program covers all aspects related to training a customer and the organization's own employees on the organization's products. This includes, but is not limited to, identifying required customer training courses, determining course objectives and course content, determining logistics associated with each course (for example, duration, frequency of offering, and cost), creating audience tracks for each course, developing the course material, providing the training, and collecting and acting upon student feedback on the courses.

Professional Services. Professional services, when provided by an organization, entails providing product customization and deployment support as per a customer's unique requirements. It includes but is not limited to: identification of specific requirements for the professional services assignment, and creation of a formal statement of work; agreement on acceptance criteria for completion of the assignment; execution of all software development and testing tasks for customization and deployment of the product at the customer site; and, finally, handoff of relevant project documentation and final knowledge transfer to the customer. It is also worth mentioning that, typically, organizations separately classify such customized software in order to differentiate it from the software delivered with the core product. In other words, the *final solution* that is deployed at the customer site may comprise two types of software:

- The core software product provided "as is" by the vendor

- Customizations or enhancements to the core product so that it fits into the customer's specific operational environment

Both of these software products are covered by separate contracts and maintenance agreements, thus requiring them to be classified and configuration controlled separately.

Customer Service. This process begins after release of the product to the customer and constitutes the maintenance phase of the product. It covers all aspects related to customer calls management (or customer's request for service), and certain aspects of customer communication (refer to explanation of subclause 7.2.3). The calls-management process begins with the receipt of a customer-reported problem, request for product information, or miscellaneous request (such as a complaint or a product change request). In the case of a reported problem, it progresses through the traditional defect management process resulting in a defect fix being delivered to the customer as a software patch, or in a normally scheduled major or minor release of the product. For a product change request—request for change in current functionality or request for new functionality—it progresses through the product change request process, which includes agreement on time and cost for the requested change. This may result in the assignment of the change request to the current release or a future release. In case of a customer complaint, it progresses through a customer complaint handling and corrective action process. In case of a request for product information, it is usually handled directly by the customer service staff that collects and provides the requested information to the customer.

The Software Product Development Process

The bulk of the requirements in ISO 9001:2000 pertain to the SPDP (an example of an SPDP is shown in Figure 3.5). This process may be defined as:

☞ A step-by-step process that results in the transformation of specified product requirements into a software product *(product realization)* by means of requirements specification, software design, implementation, integration, and testing. This process also comprises ancillary management and support processes to guide and support its execution.

The SPDP essentially comprises three main types of processes that are described next: management processes, software development lifecycle (SDLC), and support processes. Be aware that because the management and support processes are closely entwined with the SDLC, their significance in impacting overall project success cannot be overlooked. For example, a project team comprising excellent technical personnel is bound to fail in achieving all its goals if it is poorly managed and controlled. It is for this reason that there are requirements pertaining to these processes in ISO 9001:2000. The SPDP is now explained in greater depth:

1. *Management Processes.* These comprise processes for the management of software product development, including but not limited to processes for project planning, project tracking and control, and product management.

The project planning process entails the creation of feasible project plans, including but not limited to: effort estimates, project schedule, resource requirements (including third-party hardware and software requirements), personnel allocation, required project deliverables, project milestones, and initial identification of project risks. Project tracking and control processes provide visibility into project progress by means of regular cross-functional project meetings and other informal meetings, milestone reviews, everyday

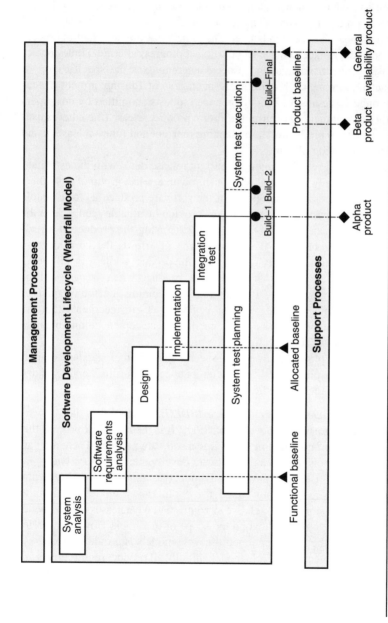

Figure 3.5 Software product development process map.

issue tracking and resolution (by assignment of action items to appropriate personnel), and timely identification of new risks and discussion on risk mitigation and contingency strategies. In addition, there is generally a formal process for requesting and executing needed changes to the previously agreed project scope, schedule, and budget. The project tracking and control process also includes management review of project progress at critical milestones.

The product management process encompasses the specification of product requirements; requirements management (during project execution); ongoing review of product change requests submitted by customers and their assignment to a current or future product release (the latter is usually preferable); product release planning (current and future releases); and product end-of-life planning.

Product release planning for a current release deals with the establishment of a mutually beneficial relationship with a select group of customers who may be provided a prerelease of the software product, as for example via a "beta program." Such prereleases provide invaluable feedback to the organization because it is obtained from exercising the product in a real-world-like environment.[7] At the same time, it affords the customers an opportunity to provide early feedback on the product while it is still being developed, and positively influence the product when it can still be improved relatively easily. Product release planning for future releases entails establishing a road map for key product enhancements that are planned for future releases. This facilitates customer communication regarding the intended direction of the product.

End-of-life planning covers all aspects of duration of standard support for a product, its planned date of discontinuance (end of life), and extended support beyond the end-of-life date.

2. *Software Development Lifecycle (SDLC).* The SDLC is the software engineering process embedded in the SPDP. It is the *technical* process that transforms the product requirements into a software product. There are various SDLC models in use in the software development industry, but by far the most widely used are the waterfall model (explained later), incremental model (and a slight variant called the evolutionary model), and spiral model. A discussion on the relative strengths and weaknesses of one model compared to the others is beyond the scope of this book. However, a brief introduction to the aforementioned lifecycle models is provided next.

In an incremental lifecycle model, initially all product requirements are identified and the overall architecture of the product is established, but detailed design, coding, integration, and testing are distributed over several *increments* (executed in parallel or in sequence). Each increment adds to functionality developed in previous increments, and is integrated and tested with functionality developed in previous increments. In this manner, the final increment results in the delivery of the complete product that satisfies all product requirements (see Figure 3.6).

The evolutionary lifecycle model is very similar to the incremental model, with two key distinguishing factors: 1) all increments are necessarily sequential, and 2) customer evaluation feedback on the output of each increment is used to identify requirements for subsequent increments, and it may cause refinement of requirements for a delivered increment. In essence, the evolutionary lifecycle model uses development experience from earlier increments to help define requirements for subsequent increments.

The spiral lifecycle model was specifically developed to incorporate risk assessment into the software development lifecycle.[8] It is yet another model of evolutionary software development. It begins with initial *planning* and requirements identification, followed by *risk analysis* based on the identified requirements, *engineering*[9] of the product (or a prototype), and *customer evaluation* of the product (or prototype), followed by replanning and refinement of requirements as per evaluation feedback from the

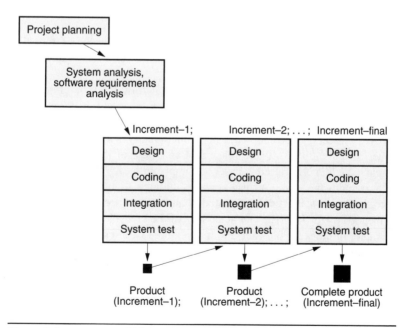

Figure 3.6   Incremental lifecycle model.

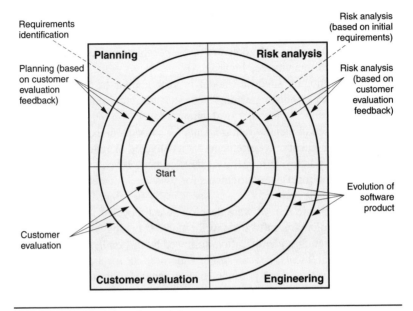

Figure 3.7 Spiral lifecycle model.

customer, and repetition of the previous cycle (see Figure 3.7). Gradually, with each spiral, the preliminary product or prototype evolves toward the complete product.

The type of lifecycle model used is dictated by the type of software development project and product the model is to be used for. For example, in large system development that is time-to-market critical, an incremental lifecycle model may be adopted, where functionality is delivered to the customer over multiple software releases. Regardless of the lifecycle model employed, what is required in order to comply with each ISO 9000 requirement remains the same. What may vary, although slightly, is *how* compliance is to be achieved to a stated requirement, because this will be influenced by the intrinsic characteristics of the lifecycle model in use. For example, in the waterfall lifecycle model, there is, in essence, one system test phase to validate the product design against requirements. On the other hand, in an incremental lifecycle process, there are multiple system test phases wherein piecemeal requirements validation is performed because the requirements are incrementally implemented over multiple phases. Due to the relatively minor and intuitive nature of these variations, discussion on these would be peripheral to the content of this book. However, it is important to be cognizant of the fact that how compliance to a particular requirement is to be achieved has to be adapted according to the particular lifecycle model in use.

☞   For the purpose of this book, a waterfall lifecycle model *with feedback* is assumed (see Figure 3.5). In the waterfall lifecycle model, software development for the *complete product* progresses sequentially through system analysis, software requirements analysis, software design, implementation, integration test, and system test subprocesses. *With feedback* implies that there may be possible feedback from a subsequent subprocess in the lifecycle, to a previous one. Such a model is more representative of the real world. For example, during the design subprocess, a need for requirement clarification may be identified; therefore, this may necessitate a revision to the software requirements specification created in the software requirements analysis subprocess. During later discussions in this book, no bias is intended toward a particular type of organizational structure, product domain within the software industry, or product development process.

Following is a quick overview[10] of each of the subprocesses in Figure 3.5:

System Analysis. Software delivered to a customer may be *the final system*, or it may be *part of* the final system. For example, the product may comprise hardware and software. The purpose of this phase is to establish the operational requirements for the final system (or product) in a PRD. As stated earlier, this step may be performed earlier in the meta-process if there is a need for greater depth of requirements definition for the purpose of contractual negotiations or finalization of project plans. A separate high-level design document may be created at this stage to lay out the high-level system architecture, or the architecture may be included in the requirements document. Such a high-level design helps in requirements analysis by facilitating a better understanding of the product, and, more importantly, it can help in the identification of additional requirements for the product, its subsystems, and its interfaces. During this phase, a subset of the system requirements that are to be met by the software are allocated to it. The requirements document is formally reviewed and approved by the customer and the supplier. In the case of contract-based companies, "customer" refers to the final customer who is buying the product. In the case of product-based companies, there is an internal as well as an external customer. The internal customer typically is the product's marketing department, represented by the product manager, while the external customer is the final customer buying the product. For the purpose of requirements approval, however, it is generally sufficient for the product manager to fulfill the role of customer.

Software Requirements Analysis. The purpose of this phase is to further break down the system requirements into atomic requirements that can be implemented and tested. If applicable, design constraints may also be specified at this stage. Software requirements analysis is generally performed by the software engineers or system engineers, and it results in the creation of a software requirements specification (SRS). As in the case of the PRD, the SRS is formally reviewed and approved by the customer and supplier. Again, depending on the situation, the customer may be the end customer or an internal customer. Note that the SRS review is a cross-functional review and appropriate departments, such as system test, technical publications, and quality assurance, are also invited.

Software Design. The purpose of this phase is to create a detailed software design document that includes information such as software design architecture, software subsystems, interfaces, processing, and error-handling mechanisms (refer to Software Design Document template in appendix B). Software design is performed by the software engineers. The output of this phase is a software design document (SDD) that is formally reviewed and approved with the organization that authored the parent SRS. Other departments, as appropriate, are invited to the review. Also during this phase, the technical writers may create a separate design document for the product documentation to be delivered to the customer.

Implementation. The purpose of this phase is to implement the software design as documented in the SDD (coding), and to produce a first version of the product documentation and online help. Coding is performed by the software engineers by following the guidelines in the organization's software coding standard, and the implemented code is exercised by unit testing (primarily white-box), unit-level integration testing, and code reviews with peer developers, system engineers, and maintenance engineers. All software development is performed in a configuration-controlled environment. Also, during this phase, the first version of the product documentation undergoes a technical review with the software developers and other appropriate departments.

Integration Test. During this phase, unit-tested software modules that represent complete functions or components of the software product are incrementally integrated into a coherent whole to form the complete end product (or system). This phase is typically performed by software engineers who work in a separate product integration department. The software code is compiled to generate binary files for each component (software build), which are then packaged. Software development and integration is typically performed in an incremental fashion, wherein the system is partitioned into several components that are developed and integrated over several increments. Such an incremental approach helps preclude the chaos that would otherwise result if the entire system were to be developed and integrated at once. Also, during this phase, a suite of integration tests is executed in accordance with a predefined integration test plan to exercise each component and its interaction with other components, including hardware that it is being integrated with. There is also a certain amount of black-box testing performed in the form of a "minimum functional test" of the integrated product. Such a minimum functional test constitutes a sanity test of the integrated product and is the precursor to a more exhaustive system test in the next phase. Successful completion of integration tests provides assurance that the integrated product is robust enough to be subjected to thorough validation against product requirements. A successful exit from this phase, therefore, constitutes the entry criteria for the commencement of the next phase—system test of the product.

System Test Planning and Execution. The purpose of the system test phase is to validate that the product does indeed perform in accordance with its intended use. For this purpose, the product is tested against documented product requirements by exercising it in a test environment that emulates the operational environment of the customer(s). Successful completion of system test provides a high degree of assurance that the finished product will work as desired in the real world.

The system test planning phase begins early, typically in the software requirements analysis phase. Initially, test engineers participate in the review of system and software requirements to ensure that they are unambiguous, easily understandable, and testable, such that success or failure of a test case can be easily ascertained. During system test planning, a test plan is generated that outlines the objective of the testing, limitation and risks (if any), types of tests that will be performed (including product documentation testing), test environment, list of test cases to be executed along with detailed test steps, test data, and expected results. If appropriate, the test cases may be contained in an ancillary document. All test cases are formally traced to requirements to ensure that all requirements are adequately tested during system test. The test plan is reviewed with representatives from departments such as product marketing, software engineering, technical publications, and quality assurance. During test execution, anomalies in product behavior are formally logged and reported via a problem-reporting mechanism. Reported problems are resolved by the software engineers, and the software is rebuilt and delivered to system test for retesting. The product is retested to ensure that reported defects have been resolved and to confirm that new defects have not been introduced in previously correct functionality (verified by means of regression testing). Remaining system tests are then executed until system test exit criteria are met.

Note that upon successful completion of system test and after release of the product to the customer, the customer generally runs acceptance tests to test the product in the pre-production environment. Acceptance testing comprises tests such as installation tests, configuration tests, user-interface tests, use-case[11] tests, and performance tests. Successful completion of acceptance tests and achievement of product acceptance criteria previously agreed to between the customer and its supplier signals the customer's acceptance of the product for operational use.

3. Support processes. As the name suggests, these comprise ancillary processes, or functions, that are required to support the processes in the SDLC. A brief description of typical support processes in software development organizations is provided next. Further discussion on these topics can be found later in this book, under the explanation of the applicable ISO 9001:2000 requirements.

Configuration Management. Configuration management is a discipline for identifying the components and associated documentation of a product in order to control changes made to them, and to maintain traceability during the SDLC. The purpose of configuration management is to establish and maintain the integrity of all artifacts produced during the SPDP, provide information on the status and version of the product to facilitate use of appropriate versions of items, and prevent unauthorized changes to artifacts. Because effective configuration management has a direct influence on the integrity and quality of products delivered to the customer, it is viewed as a critical element of the QMS.

The four key functions within configuration management are:

• *Configuration identification.* Configuration identification is accomplished by means of a configuration item (CI) naming convention, and it supports the unique identification of each intermediate or final artifact in the SPDP, for example, SRS, SDD, code, test cases, and so on.

The definition of configuration management (CM) baselines is also covered by this function. CM baselines provide a snapshot of all approved project and product documentation and records at specific points in the SPDP. The CM baselines that are most widely used are functional baseline, allocated baseline, and product baseline (refer to Figure 3.5, page 53).

A functional baseline is the first formal baseline and it establishes the product requirements. Key elements of this baseline are the PRDs, and project plan(s). This baseline is established at the successful completion of the system analysis phase.

An allocated baseline establishes the allocation of product requirements to the product design. Key elements of this baseline are design document(s), and it is established at the end of the design phase. It also includes new project documents approved after the functional baseline, and updated versions, if any, of previously baselined documents.

A product baseline is established upon completion of system test activities and it comprises the final version of the product, product documentation, and project documentation. It also includes new project documents approved after the allocated baseline (for example, system test reports), and updated versions, if any, of previously baselined documents.

In addition to the aforementioned baselines, an organization may define additional CM baselines to correspond to the end of each phase in the SDLC. Overall, CM baselines provide valuable information on not only what approved project documents were available at a specific point in the process, but they also provide insight into document evolution from one baseline to the next.

• *Configuration (or change) control.* Configuration control is accomplished by means of a configuration control board (CCB). The CCB reviews and dispositions changes requested to the CIs due to reported problems as well as product change requests.

• *Configuration status accounting.* Configuration status accounting involves maintaining a record of the current status and history of changes for each CI.

• *Configuration audits.* Configuration audits help verify whether the CIs have been built in accordance with applicable requirements and established standards. These include functional and physical configuration audits (FCA and PCA) to verify that the CIs are functionally and physically complete and correct.

Quality Assurance. Quality assurance comprises activities that when executed provide sufficient confidence that the resulting product will comply with applicable quality requirements. The implementation of quality control and assurance activities required by ISO 9001:2000 is every employee's responsibility. However, *independent* oversight and monitoring of the implementation of quality practices in the organization, which is the subject of this discussion, is generally performed by the organization's quality department. Examples of such quality assurance activities include but are not limited to: preparation of a project quality plan[12]; participation in peer reviews of project deliverables; coordination of project and product quality measurements collection and analysis; participation in project status reviews and ongoing risk management; monitoring the deployment or piloting of lessons learned from past projects; everyday monitoring of adherence to QMS and ISO 9001:2000 requirements; and internal quality audits, such as project audits, and product audits.

Software (and Hardware) Acquisition. This process deals with the acquisition of computing hardware and/or software for the organization (refer to explanation of clause 7.4). A typical acquisition process is as follows:

The organization specifies requirements for the hardware or software to be procured; this includes not only functional and nonfunctional requirements, but also business requirements such as cost and terms of support and maintenance. Market research is conducted to identify viable candidate products, followed by a preliminary review to arrive at a short list of the products to be considered further in the acquisition process. If appropriate, the short-listed products are procured for an on-site evaluation. An exhaustive comparative assessment of the short-listed products is performed against established criteria (including comparison of business terms) before arriving at the purchase decision.

Physical Infrastructure. This function deals with providing a physical infrastructure, including information technology (IT), which provides adequate work environment and support for the execution of the SPDP. This includes but is not limited to: physical workspace and furnishings, fax machines, printers, copiers, phones, desktop and laptop computers, servers, routers, databases, operating systems, and office automation software. This function typically owns the critical organizational process of disaster recovery. Any scenario that causes a prolonged business interruption may be viewed as a disaster that requires advance planning for contingency measures. Examples include: limited or significant damage to a facility due to environmental catastrophes or accidents, power outage, or security breach of a facility. The disaster recovery plan specifies the recovery process, roles and responsibilities, and schedules to minimize the impact of disaster scenarios and facilitate rapid recovery in the event of a disaster.

Employee Training. This function deals with identifying training needs for employees, providing the needed training, and maintaining employee training records. This includes product training, technical training, and soft skills training. Need for employee training may be identified at the time of annual performance review, and it should be identified throughout the year—when the employee is provided a new assignment, is promoted, is transferred, or generally needs to upgrade his or her skills. Training may be imparted by various vehicles such as Web-based training (WBT), computer-based training (CBT), classroom study, self study, on-the-job training, conferences and seminars, tutorials, mentoring, or continuing education at college or university. Many organizations use a formal mentoring program wherein an experienced employee contributes to the development of a less experienced employee on technical, business, and personal levels.

In addition to these phases and processes in the SPDP, the SPDP also contains milestones for the review of project progress at predefined points. A milestone represents an important and measurable intermediate objective that must be achieved at that point in the process. Milestone review meetings are coordinated by the project manager, with participation of appropriate departments, and they constitute a detailed review of the project status against plans to authorize further progress of a project, and to facilitate timely corrective and preventive actions.

The SPDP also supports the following types of commonly prevalent product releases: alpha, beta, and GA. An *alpha release* typically represents a product that has undergone complete unit and integration testing, and is released for internal testing by other members of the organization, or is released to the customer to elicit early feedback on the product (or for other reasons); a *beta release* typically denotes a product that has undergone sufficient system testing, although not necessarily complete, and is released to a customer to exercise the product in an environment similar to the real-world operational environment; and a *GA release* denotes a product that has undergone complete system test, and has met final release criteria for the product. It is recognized that some variations of what constitutes an alpha or beta release do exist in the software industry. In all cases, each of these product releases is generally preceded by a successful milestone review authorizing release of the product.

Establishing ISO 9001:2000 Registration Scope

There are two key items that an organization needs to address when implementing ISO 9001:2000:

- First, it needs to clearly define the scope of its planned ISO 9001:2000 registration.

- Second, within the identified scope of the registration, the organization needs to comply with all *applicable* requirements of ISO 9001:2000.

When an organization implements a QMS as per ISO 9001:2000 requirements, its QMS does not have to encompass the entire organization. That is, not all the organization's locations and products have to be in the scope of the ISO 9000 registration. ISO 9001:2000 provides organizations the freedom to define the scope of their QMS. Therefore, an organization may choose to stagger its QMS implementation, wherein the initial ISO 9000 registration may cover only some of the organization's locations and products. Subsequently, after the three-year registration period, when the ISO 9000 registration is due for renewal, the organization may choose to enhance the scope of its registration to cover additional locations and products. On the other hand, an organization may also choose to never enhance the scope of its initial ISO 9000 registration. There are numerous factors that may influence the decision regarding what registration scope an organization chooses. Some of these are: business need (return on investment considerations), customer requirement for registration, product marketing need, and level of maturity of the organization's products and/or locations. Some situations where these factors may come into play include:

- In the case of a multiproduct organization, customers buying a particular product may require that the associated SPDP be ISO 9000 registered.

- An organization that is not previously registered to ISO 9000, when introducing a new product in the market, may want to achieve registration for its new product's development process only. This may help the organization in its marketing effort by providing a certain amount of assurance to potential customers regarding the new product's quality.

- In the case of a multisite organization, certain locations may have a higher process maturity compared to others. It may be a good idea to register these locations to ISO 9000 and apply the experience gained and lessons learned to subsequently register other office locations as well.

☞ The scope of an organization's ISO 9000 registration must be clearly documented in its quality manual (as per subclause 4.2.2). The ISO 9000 registration certificate issued to the organization clearly states the scope of the registration. Any external communication and publications of the organization regarding its ISO 9000 registration should clearly state the scope of its registration, so as not to confuse customers and other parties.

If the organization needs to change its registration scope *after* successfully registering to ISO 9000—a change that may be necessitated by events such as introduction of new products (or discontinuance of old products), mergers and acquisitions, and opening of new office locations—then the original registration scope *may* be changed. However, in such a situation, any new areas proposed for inclusion in the scope of the registration would have to be audited by the registrar. If an organization foresees such a situation, it should contact its registrar to determine how its registration would be impacted so it can use that information for planning future strategy.

Permissible Exclusions from Registration

With the publication of ISO 9001:2000, the old ISO 9000 standards (ISO 9001:1994, ISO 9002:1994, and ISO 9003:1994) became obsolete by December 15, 2003. ISO 9002:1994 and ISO 9003:1994 were created because ISO/TC 176 realized that due to the unique nature of every organization's business and customer requirements, all of the requirements contained in ISO 9001:1994 might not be applicable to all organizations. ISO 9002:1994 and ISO 9003:1994 helped accommodate such organizations by allowing them to obtain an ISO 9000 registration even though all the requirements contained in the standard did not apply to them. For example, the ISO 9002:1994 standard was identical to ISO 9001:1994, except for the exclusion of element 4.4—Design Control. Therefore, organizations that did not perform design and development activities were registered to the ISO 9002:1994 standard.

Fundamentally, the ISO 9002:1994 and ISO 9003:1994 standards were subsets of the ISO 9001:1994 standard. ISO/TC 176 members agreed that due to this subset relationship of the standards, they could easily discontinue ISO 9002 and ISO 9003 by allowing "permissible exclusions" in the parent standard ISO 9001. This meant that organizations pursuing an ISO 9000 registration would be permitted to exclude those activities (requirements) in the standard that did not apply to their business.

This approach was adopted for the first time in ISO 9001:2000 with the inclusion of clause 1.2—Application, which allows permissible exclusions only within a specific set of QMS requirements. These are those requirements that are included under clause 7 (Product Realization) of the standard. Note that, as per subclause 4.2.2, an organization choosing to exclude compliance to any clause 7 requirement(s) must identify them, along with supporting rationale, in its quality manual.

☞ It is strongly recommended that the organization also discuss such exclusions in advance with its registrar. This will help preclude any potential disagreements with the auditor during the registration audit.

Recommended Implementation Process

At the time when preliminary[13] implementation planning for ISO 9000 is initiated, the management representative should ensure that the implementation team members are provided formal training on the ISO 9001:2000 standard. Adequate familiarity with the standard's requirements will enable the team members to better understand the scope of the task on hand, and thus help in the establishment of a more realistic implementation plan. Such training may be provided by an outside vendor or a qualified in-house instructor. Personnel should not only be educated on the standard and its requirements, but they should also be educated on the relevance of the standard to the organization's business, benefits of achieving registration, and how the standard will affect different departments in the organization. Once trained, the implementation team members can then train all employees in the organization before implementation begins.

As part of the preliminary implementation planning, the overall implementation process should also be defined. Following a systematic approach to ISO 9000 implementation, where the implementation progresses through distinct phases, each with its own unique purpose, helps keep the organization focused during the implementation. This can be achieved by decomposing the registration goal into intermediate goals that constitute the objectives for each implementation phase. The organization can then proceed to systematically conquer and celebrate the achievement of these intermediate goals, as it drives toward the registration goal. Different organizations may follow a process that is a slight variant of the process described next, but the implementation phases are essentially as follows:

- QMS definition
- QMS refinement
- QMS deployment
- QMS registration

QMS Definition Phase

The QMS definition phase is the most critical phase and it entails defining the QMS as per ISO 9001:2000 requirements. This phase includes the following key activities:

1. Analysis of each ISO 9001:2000 requirement to clearly understand what is required and how the requirement can be satisfied.

2. Identification of all organizational processes within the registration scope.

3. Preliminary[14] gap analysis to determine what ISO 9001:2000 requirements are already being addressed, in whole or in part, in the current way of working. When appropriate, reuse all or part of the current implementation as opposed to beginning from scratch.

4. Refinement of the preliminary implementation plan by using the information obtained from the preliminary gap analysis.

5. Implementation of ISO 9001:2000 requirements that are not currently being addressed, and enhancement of the current implementation in cases where the current implementation is partially compliant with ISO 9001:2000 requirements. For this purpose, it is recommended that at least a two-level prioritization be performed of the requirements that need to be met and the associated QMS documentation that needs to be created. For example, definition of the internal audits procedure may be addressed after the relatively higher priority task of defining product realization processes has been completed. Similarly, identification of process metrics should be addressed after the related process has been defined. For each requirement to be implemented, it should be assigned to the PGM who is (or represents) the process owner[15] for the associated process. As each requirement is implemented and associated QMS documentation is prepared, it should be verified for correctness and validated for compliance to applicable ISO 9001:2000 requirements.

QMS Refinement Phase

The QMS refinement phase involves a final verification across the entire QMS to ensure that all processes interact as originally planned, and further, the processes are mutually consistent and correctly defined. This phase also involves a final validation to ensure *all* elements of the QMS comply with ISO 9001:2000 requirements. Note that while the focus in the definition phase is on *initial verification and validation of individual elements of the QMS* as they are defined, the focus in this phase shifts to *final verification and validation of the complete QMS*. This provides a high degree of assurance that all ISO 9001:2000 requirements have been adequately addressed across the entire QMS, and none have fallen through the cracks.

QMS Deployment Phase

The QMS deployment phase involves promulgating the defined system to all employees by means of vehicles, such as use of the corporate intranet (or a similar shared and easily accessible repository) for publishing the QMS documentation, conducting employee training, and performing internal quality audits to verify whether the implemented system is being adhered to. It is important to plan for a certain amount of time between completion of the employee training and commencement of internal quality audits. This time period, referred to as *process establishment* in Figure 3.8, is required to adequately disseminate the QMS processes throughout the organization—such that it gets well entrenched in the organization by becoming an inherent part of how everyday business is conducted. In other

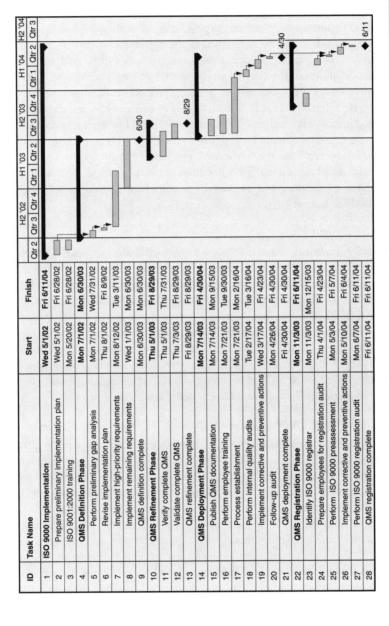

ID	Task Name	Start	Finish
1	**ISO 9000 Implementation**	**Wed 5/1/02**	**Fri 6/11/04**
2	Prepare preliminary implementation plan	Wed 5/1/02	Fri 6/28/02
3	ISO 9001:2000 training	Mon 5/20/02	Fri 6/28/02
4	**QMS Definition Phase**	**Mon 7/1/02**	**Mon 6/30/03**
5	Perform preliminary gap analysis	Mon 7/1/02	Wed 7/31/02
6	Revise implementation plan	Thu 8/1/02	Fri 8/9/02
7	Implement high-priority requirements	Mon 8/12/02	Tue 3/11/03
8	Implement remaining requirements	Wed 1/1/03	Mon 6/30/03
9	QMS definition complete	Mon 6/30/03	Mon 6/30/03
10	**QMS Refinement Phase**	**Thu 5/1/03**	**Fri 8/29/03**
11	Verify complete QMS	Thu 5/1/03	Thu 7/31/03
12	Validate complete QMS	Thu 7/3/03	Fri 8/29/03
13	QMS refinement complete	Fri 8/29/03	Fri 8/29/03
14	**QMS Deployment Phase**	**Mon 7/14/03**	**Fri 4/30/04**
15	Publish QMS documentation	Mon 7/14/03	Mon 9/15/03
16	Perform employee training	Mon 7/21/03	Tue 9/30/03
17	Process establishment	Mon 7/21/03	Mon 2/16/04
18	Perform internal quality audits	Tue 2/17/04	Tue 3/16/04
19	Implement corrective and preventive actions	Wed 3/17/04	Fri 4/23/04
20	Follow-up audit	Mon 4/26/04	Fri 4/30/04
21	QMS deployment complete	Fri 4/30/04	Fri 4/30/04
22	**QMS Registration Phase**	**Mon 11/3/03**	**Fri 6/11/04**
23	Identify ISO 9000 registrar	Mon 11/3/03	Mon 12/15/03
24	Prepare employees for registration audit	Thu 4/1/04	Fri 4/23/04
25	Perform ISO 9000 preassessment	Mon 5/3/04	Fri 5/7/04
26	Implement corrective and preventive actions	Mon 5/10/04	Fri 6/4/04
27	Perform ISO 9000 registration audit	Mon 6/7/04	Fri 6/11/04
28	QMS registration complete	Fri 6/11/04	Fri 6/11/04

Figure 3.8 Gantt chart for ISO 9000 implementation project phases and milestone dates.

words, use of the QMS *gradually* becomes second nature to the employees. A second reason this time period is needed is that it helps build sufficient evidence of use of the QMS that can then be audited. Starting an internal quality audit program too soon may not provide the internal auditors the critical mass of evidence that is necessary to adequately determine whether the QMS is being adhered to. The time required for process establishment in an organization will vary according to factors such as:

- *Release cycle time.*[16] Release cycle time has a bearing on process establishment time because all elements of the QMS, including those pertaining to product realization processes, need to be executed at least once in a software development project. Therefore, the greater the release cycle time, more is the time needed to exercise all elements of the QMS at least once.

- *Number of projects in execution.* Whether the organization executes one project at a time or multiple projects simultaneously (in different stages of execution) has a bearing on process establishment time. This is because if an organization has more than one project in execution in different stages of development, then it has the opportunity to begin a simultaneous rollout of the QMS in different projects, and obtain experience from its use. On the contrary, if the organization executes only one project at any given time, then depending on what stage the project has reached in the overall lifecycle, the organization may not be able to roll out all QMS processes. For example, if the project currently being executed is entering the system test phase, then only the QMS processes from the system test phase (and forward) may be rolled out, and the organization would have to wait until the launch of the next project to roll out QMS processes that occur before the system test phase (such as, the project planning process).

- *Extent and complexity of change to established processes.* Implementation of ISO 9000 requirements invariably results in a change to an organization's processes. The extent of this change will depend on how much out of alignment with ISO 9000 requirements the organization's current processes are. The more is the misalignment, more is the extent of change required to make them compliant with ISO 9000 requirements, and consequently, more is the time required for establishing the modified processes. Further, the complexity of changes also has a bearing on the amount of time required to promulgate the changes in the organization, and to get the employees accustomed to work with the new and modified processes.

- *Quality and extent of training provided to employees.* Inadequate or insufficient training on QMS processes may cause difficulties in executing the processes, which may lead to a need for additional training, and, consequently, more time for process establishment.

QMS Registration Phase

QMS registration is the final phase, and it covers the ISO 9000 registration process. This includes following a systematic approach to selecting the ISO 9000 registrar, initiating the registration process with the registrar, preparing the organization for the registration audit, and, finally, the registration audit itself.

Each of the implementation phases should have an identified due date for completion. These dates serve as the phase completion milestones for the project. If required, additional milestones may be defined for critical activities to be performed in each implementation phase. An example of an ISO 9000 implementation schedule with the aforementioned implementation phases and milestones is shown in Figure 3.8.

☞ The Gantt chart shown in Figure 3.8 is *not* intended to imply a strictly sequential flow of activities; it is only intended to depict the *logical flow* of activities that are generally necessary in implementing a QMS. Typically, several activities during the implementation will be executed in an iterative and overlapped fashion. For example, experience from use of a new process will typically result in feedback on what works and what does not work, and, consequently, there may be a need for changes to the process and associated QMS documentation. This may necessitate formal retraining of employees on the revised process, or at least, that they be made aware of the changes by being provided revised QMS documentation. Keep in mind that organizations' processes continue to evolve forever—even after ISO 9000 registration (as a natural consequence of process improvement efforts). However, the degree of change is greater initially because processes take time to stabilize to a state where their capabilities are fully determined (from past experience) and they have been sufficiently refined that they can consistently meet expectations.

On a final note, as with any *plan* document, the implementation plan established at this stage of the implementation is subject to future revisions and should be actively maintained. The implementation plan should be revised as and when appropriate, once the implementation gets underway and new information becomes available. At any given time, current situation or extenuating circumstances may necessitate a replanning of certain activities, or identification of new activities to be performed. The implementation plan should reflect current realities and should be feasible, given current circumstances in the organization. It may also be used as a progress tracking tool to reflect tasks completed and status of those in progress.

A word of caution: It is important that sufficient thought be given to identifying the activities to be performed in each phase. This is because once the implementation team has a good idea of precisely what each phase entails, including the time required to perform the activities, only then can realistic project milestone dates be established. Because most of the key activities for ISO 9000 implementation are actually an aggregation of a number of subtasks, therefore, in order to determine the time needed to complete an activity, the time needed for completing each of its constituent subtasks will have to be carefully considered. For example, if an activity for ISO 9000 implementation is "Document all required quality procedures," then, before a time frame can be allocated for this activity, the implementation team will have to determine how much time is typically required to document a single procedure, and approximately how many procedures need to be documented. The time required to document each procedure may be obtained experientially, or by documenting two or three procedures as a sample.

Finally, bear in mind that ISO 9000 implementation requires the implementation team to assume a consulting role for daily activities. This includes: responding to employee queries regarding ISO 9000; explaining the rationale behind the ISO 9000 requirements; helping employees define their processes and prepare adequate documentation; and mentoring them as they start performing their daily operations in compliance with ISO 9000. Time requirements for such consulting tasks have planning implications in terms of how much overall time would be required for a successful ISO 9000 implementation. Time requirements for mentoring the PGMs and employees will need to be considered while preparing the ISO 9000 implementation schedule, along with time requirements for routine activities, such as coordination meetings of the implementation team, progress tracking, and status reporting to management and employees.

Quality Management System Documentation

Before discussing the standard's requirements in detail, it is necessary that a key aspect of any successful ISO 9000 implementation be discussed— that is *QMS documentation*. This is because, as we all know, one of the most significant tasks during an ISO 9000 implementation is preparation of required[17] QMS documentation. It is therefore very important that the implementation team have a rational approach and a common understanding regarding the extent and depth of required documentation. Often, organizations adopt a flawed approach to documenting their QMS. On one end of the spectrum, there are organizations that develop an unnecessarily detailed and complex system of QMS documents that document every level of detail and thus frequently must be updated to account for minute operational or organizational changes. On the other end, there are organizations that with the sole intention of barely passing an ISO 9000 audit create only the minimum set of required QMS documents. These documents are generically worded and intentionally vague, with the supporting rationale being: "If our documents are so worded that each sentence provides us room for escape, the auditor will not be able to pin us down on any specific item. We will therefore be able to pass the ISO 9000 audit." Such reasoning obviously defeats the very intent of ISO 9000 and reflects an organization's shallow commitment to quality. As described in this section, the recommended level of detail in the QMS documents is somewhere in between these two extremes. This section also includes useful tips and guidelines for creating QMS documentation.

Documentation Strategy

ISO 9001:2000 encourages organizations to take a process-based approach when implementing their QMS. This means that first and foremost you should take a *process-based view* toward your QMS, and not a *clause-based view*. That is, do *not* start creating QMS documents separately for each clause of ISO 9001:2000 to describe how the requirements in that clause are implemented in your organization. Instead, first conceptualize the key business processes of your organization that interact to result in the delivery of your organization's products. Next, physically represent these high-level organizational processes by means of *process mapping*. Process mapping entails pictorially depicting an organization's processes (refer to examples of process maps in Figures 3.4 and 3.5, pages 48 and 53, respectively). This task is simplified if the process is bounded as an end-to-end process—starting with requirements receipt from customer, and ending with product delivery to the customer. The high-level process map should depict the sequence and interaction of all the high-level business processes, and it should also reflect the general start and end time frames for each of the processes. Bear in mind that business processes in today's organizations are rarely executed sequentially. They are either executed in parallel or they are partially overlapped— that is, before one process is complete, the initial activities of the subsequent process have already begun. It is necessary to keep these considerations in mind while defining the process map.

The importance of the process mapping exercise should not be overlooked. It provides the ISO 9000 implementation team a good starting point by familiarizing them with the organization's business processes, their sequence, interfaces, and interaction. It enables the organization to understand the scope of its ISO 9000 implementation effort vis-à-vis its business processes. Most importantly, it enables the organization to develop and discuss its QMS in the context of its business processes, which is the underlying theme of ISO 9001:2000.

A frequently encountered pitfall in ISO 9000 implementations is that of creating *excess documentation*. Subclause 4.2.1 specifies the documentation requirements of the standard and it counters the myth that ISO 9000 requires a complex system of detailed QMS documents. Organizations typically end up with a complex system of documents if they adopt a "bottom-up" approach to implementing their QMS where they begin by documenting each activity that is executed, as opposed to the desirable "top-down" approach. The top-down implementation approach entails identifying and documenting the highest-level QMS processes (facilitated by process mapping), followed by identification and documentation of subprocesses at the next lower level *(only to the extent needed),* and so on until the lowest level at which all the day-to-day tasks are executed. Note that the key words here are *only to the extent needed.* Specifically, this means that unless a QMS document is explicitly required by ISO 9001:2000, organizations have the freedom to determine, based on their perceived need, what QMS documentation needs to be created. In essence, the *added value* of documenting a process should always be considered before the decision to document it. The amount of detail included in different QMS documents may vary—unless a particular ISO 9001:2000 requirement specifically requires that certain information be documented (for example, subclauses 8.5.2 and 8.5.3 contain specific requirements regarding the expected content in an organization's corrective and preventive action procedures). In fact, subclause 4.2.1 clarifies that the extent of QMS documentation is dictated by factors such as the size of the organization, type of activities, the complexity of the process being documented, and competency level of employees executing the process. Therefore, if an organization requires a QMS document for the effective planning, operation, and control of a process, then it must create that document. For example, ISO 9001:2000 does not require that an organization's unit test process be formally documented. However, if an organization has observed from past internal quality audits that there have been frequent process breakdowns in unit testing, or there has been a significant inconsistency in how unit testing is performed, then it would strongly indicate a need to document the process. In addition, relevant employees must be trained on the documented process in order to ensure improved process adherence and consistency in process execution (as per subclause 6.2.2).

Another question that some organizations may have is: "If we already have some QMS documentation in place to describe their business processes, can we reuse and/or modify this documentation to comply with ISO 9001:2000 requirements?" Sure. In fact, opportunities to maximize reuse of existing QMS documentation should be explored. This is because the organization's employees are already familiar with this documentation and are accustomed to using it. Moreover, keep in mind that ISO 9000 is *not* a prescriptive standard. In that, it specifies what requirements shall be complied with, but it does not specify how to comply with those requirements—that is entirely the organization's prerogative. Therefore, if an existing QMS document fully complies with a stated ISO 9000 requirement, then it may be reused as is. Similarly, if a QMS document partially complies with an ISO 9000 requirement, it is advisable to modify the same document so that it fully complies with the requirement. The exercise of determining what QMS documents required by ISO 9000 currently exist in the organization, and assessing the extent of their compliance with the standard is performed during preliminary gap analysis in the QMS definition phase.

Essential Elements of a Documentation System

Now that you are ready to begin creating your QMS documentation, there are certain salient features of a sound documentation system that you must be familiar with. This section begins with a description of the different types of QMS documentation that are needed, followed by a description of the mechanisms required to help maintain and control QMS documentation.

Types of QMS Documents

• *Quality manual.* A quality manual is specifically required by ISO 9001:2000. It is the highest-level QMS document, and it is primarily intended to provide an overview of an organization's QMS. In case of medium and large software development organizations (say, with 100 or more employees[18]), it is preferable to exclude details regarding the organization's processes from the quality manual. Instead, such details should be embedded in the appropriate QMS documents that must be referenced, as needed, from the quality manual.[19] However, in the case of smaller software development organizations, it may be appropriate to include the procedures in the quality manual itself. Note that subclause 4.2.2 states that one of these two approaches must be adopted in creating the quality manual.

An organization's quality manual is an invaluable document for its employees, registrar, current customers, and potential customers. It should therefore reflect the organization's commitment to quality (in other words, answer *why* the organization is implementing a QMS) and describe how the organization ensures quality in its everyday operations. Senior management should realize that it is responsible for the quality manual's content. This can be demonstrated by senior management approval on the quality manual. It must be ensured that the quality manual accurately reflects the QMS and that it is kept current at all times. (Refer to related discussion on maintenance of the QMS under explanation of subclause 5.4.2, page 103.)

• *Procedures.* A procedure, also called a process definition, is a documented high-level description of a process. Procedures describe *what* activities comprise a process, *who* performs the activities, *when* the activities are performed, and *where* (department and/or location) the activities are performed (refer to procedure description template in appendix B). Procedures constitute the first level of documentation below the quality manual. Because processes in organizations typically span multiple departments, procedures are usually interdepartmental. Due to the interdepartmental nature of procedures, they should be jointly reviewed by all departments involved in the process. This helps ensure that the procedure accurately reflects the process and the interaction between various departments. As a rule of thumb, a procedure should not be longer than three pages (this only refers to the core content that describes the process). If a longer procedure is needed, it is a good candidate for splitting into separate procedures. Because a procedure is intended to contain relatively high-level information regarding a process, practitioners typically need *additional* process documents to execute their tasks—these are called *work instructions.*

• *Work instructions.* A work instruction is a documented low-level description of a process. Work instructions describe *how* activities in a process are executed, and they constitute the first level of documentation below the procedures. They provide a step-by-step description of tasks to be executed in order to accomplish each activity described in the procedure. Work instructions are typically intradepartmental and are primarily intended for use by process practitioners. Due to the intradepartmental nature of work instructions, they should be documented and jointly reviewed by the practitioners involved in executing the tasks. This is because the practitioners are generally the most knowledgeable and experienced personnel for providing this information. As a rule of thumb, work instructions should be limited to about four or five pages in length.

☞ A word on when to create work instructions: While there are certain instances where ISO 9001:2000 explicitly requires the documentation of a procedure, documentation of work instructions is not mandatory. Therefore, an organization may document work instructions on only an as-needed basis, as per subclause 4.2.1.

• *Forms and templates.* Forms and templates serve as guides for communicating the expected structure and content of a document. Therefore, they help ensure consistency within a certain type of documents. For example, for documenting procedures, it is strongly recommended that a procedure template first be established. It is also recommended that the forms and templates have brief instructions embedded in them to guide the user regarding the expected content in each section of the document. Examples of forms and templates are provided in appendix B.

☞ The *hidden text* feature in word processing software can be used for embedding such instructions as hidden text in templates and forms. Subsequently, once the document has been created, the instructions can be hidden by activating this feature.

• *Project documents and records.* Project documents[20] and records constitute the *objective evidence* to demonstrate that the QMS is being used. Once a form or template has been populated by entering the required information, it becomes a project document or a record. Therefore, project documents and records are considered types of QMS documents. For example, after a formal document review (inspection), once the "inspection form" has been duly completed, it becomes an "inspection record." Similarly, once the "project plan template" has been populated by the project manager, it becomes the "project plan" for a specific project. A project document or record thus constitutes a single instantiation of the applicable form or template, and, therefore, serves as objective evidence that the QMS is being used. Since project documents and records demonstrate conformance (or lack thereof) with the QMS, they are closely scrutinized during quality audits as part of the objective evidence examination.

In addition to the aforementioned document types, additional types of documents may exist, including: checklists, guideline documents, and workmanship standards. Examples of those include: Graphical user interface (GUI) design guidelines, software coding standard, unit testing guidelines, system test techniques, and so on. Such documents fall in the domain of "how to" documents and may be used either in addition to work instructions or in lieu of work instructions (as appropriate).

Documentation Structure

In the previous section, the description of the different types of QMS documents alludes to the logical position of each type of document in the overall documentation hierarchy of the QMS. It is best to illustrate these different levels of documentation with a quality pyramid as shown in Figure 3.9. As you go higher in the pyramid, the scope of the QMS documents widens; as you go lower in the pyramid, the scope of the QMS documents narrows, while the amount of detail in the documents and the number of documents increases. The advantage of this model is that it is intuitive and helps to quickly locate a document in the QMS, based on its content. It also serves as a useful mental reference during the creation of these documents because it guides the author regarding the expected level of detail in the document.

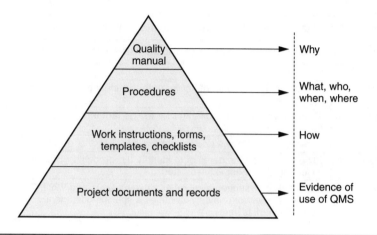

Figure 3.9 Quality pyramid.

This model is not required by ISO 9000, yet most organizations structure their QMS documentation in this way.

Document Numbering

In order to uniquely identify and control each QMS document (as required by subclause 4.2.3), a unique document number and version should be assigned to each document. For document numbering, an organizational document numbering convention should be devised. Use of the numbering scheme should be enforced by the personnel in charge of or tool used for issuing the document numbers. An example of a document numbering convention is presented in Table 3.4.a. Examples of document numbers created by following the convention in Table 3.4.a are shown in Table 3.4b.[21]

Document Versioning

Document versioning goes hand in hand with document numbering. This is because, in and of itself, a document number usually is not sufficient to uniquely identify a document; it should be supplemented with a document version number to uniquely identify the revision level of the subject document. For example, if it is stated that the currently approved version (say, version 1.0) of the system test plan BA-SYT-STP-PRB402-0021 is based on requirements stated in the document DA-SYE-SRS-PRB402-0001, it is unclear what version of the requirements document is used. This information is especially important because the system test plan might be based on

---

Table 3.4.a Example of a document numbering convention.

Document Number Format: AA-BBB-CCC-DDDDDD-XXXX

where,	
AA:	Two-character alpha identifier for organizational business unit or location
BBB:	Three-character alpha identifier for the department that owns the document
CCC:	Three-character alpha document type identifier
DDDDDD:	Six-character alpha identifier to identify the product or project with which the document is associated
XXXX:	Four-character sequential number between 0001 and 9999. This sequential number uniquely identifies a specific document (regardless of its version)

Table 3.4.b Sample document numbers (based on numbering convention in Table 3.4.a).

AA	BBB	CCC	DDDDDD	XXXX	Explanation
DA	SYE	SRS	PRB42	0001	DA-SYE-SRS-PRB42-0001 is a software requirements specification (SRS) created by the system engineering department (SYE) at the Dallas (DA) location of the organization. The SRS is for the Probe product version 4.2 (PRB42) and it is the first document (0001) created.
BA	SYT	STP	LNDR34	0009	BA-SYT-STP-LNDR34-0009 is a system test plan (STP) created by the system test department (SYT) at the Bangalore (BA) location of the organization. The system test plan is for the Lander product version 3.4 (LNDR34), and it is the ninth document (0009) created.

a version of the requirements document that has since been superseded by a subsequent version. In this case, since the system test plan version is not in harmony with its parent requirements document, it is considered obsolete and must be immediately withdrawn from use, or if it is retained for some reason, it must be marked to indicate it is obsolete to preclude its inadvertent use. It is for this reason that ISO 9001:2000 includes *control of documents* as a key requirements clause (subclause 4.2.3).

There are various document versioning conventions in use in the industry. However, the most widely used versioning convention is as follows:

Versioning of Draft Documents. During the document creation process, a document evolves through a series of *draft* versions before it is finalized and formally approved. Such draft versions of a document can be identified in one of many different ways, such as:

- Version a, version b, version c, and so on

- Draft 1, draft 2, draft 3, and so on

Versioning of the First Approved Release of a Document. Once a document has been formally approved for the first time, it should be identified by a standard version, for example, "version 1.0." This approach fosters standardization within the organization regarding versioning of approved documents and for identifying subsequent changes to them (as described next).

Versioning of Changes (or Revisions) to Approved Documents. If a formally approved document needs to be revised (and reapproved), there should be an accepted way of identifying whether the magnitude of change in the document is major or minor. In the widely used "X.Y" versioning convention, X is reserved for major changes to a document and Y is reserved for minor changes to a document. The definition of a *major change* versus a *minor change* is always subjective and different organizations develop their own definitions of these terms (which is perfectly acceptable as long as there is clear understanding and agreement within the organization). Generally, a major change implies a significant change in the document to address known errors, omissions, or required significant clarifications. Minor changes pertain to typographical and grammatical errors, or required small clarifications.

A major change to a document can be reflected in the document version by incrementing the numeric digit *before* the decimal and resetting the numeric digit *after* the decimal to zero, for example, version 1.4 → version 2.0, and version 2.0 → version 3.0. A major version number should not be skipped, for example, version 1.4 → version 3.0 is not permissible.

A minor change to a document can be reflected in the document version by incrementing the numeric digit *after* the decimal and leaving the digit *before* the decimal unchanged, for example, version 1.0 → version 1.1, and version 1.1 → version 1.2.

Instead of using the versioning convention described previously, an organization may choose some other convention as per its needs. However, it must be ensured that whatever versioning convention is used, it must be able to facilitate quick identification of the revision status of the document (as per subclause 4.2.3). It is preferable that the document version also provide a quick means of identifying a draft document versus an approved document (unless some other means is used to communicate a document's approval status). For example, "version 1.1 draft" clearly indicates the document is a draft document (not yet approved for use), while omission of the word *draft* from the document's version number may be used to indicate that the document is approved for use. In the case of a document revision, it is preferable that the document version also indicate whether the document has undergone a major revision or a minor revision (as explained earlier in this section).

Document Control

A final critical element of a sound documentation management system is document control[22] and it entails addressing each of the following items:

1. *Document review and approval.* All QMS documents must be reviewed and approved by some means before use (as per subclause 4.2.3). Documents may undergo formal or informal review. Types of reviews are discussed later under explanation of clause 7.1. As a general guideline, a document review should involve *all* its stakeholders, but the required approvals for the document should be limited to only the *key* stakeholders because an unnecessarily long list of required approvals can render the entire document approval process burdensome and time-consuming. As far as approvals are concerned, certain documents may be approved by formal means (such as signature approval), while others may be approved by informal means (such as e-mail approval), as deemed appropriate by the organization.

2. *Documents must describe the current way of working.* When documenting procedures, work instructions, and similar documents, care must be exercised to ensure that the documents describe the current way of working (such that the current way of working adequately meets ISO 9001:2000 requirements), and not how the organization would ideally like to operate in the future. This is important because during the ISO 9000 registration audit, the lead auditor will first perform a documentation audit to determine whether the QMS documentation complies with ISO 9001:2000 requirements, then the auditor will set aside the ISO 9001:2000 standard and conduct audit interviews based on the organization's own QMS documentation (see Figure 3.10). The rationale for this is that if the QMS documentation is fully compliant with ISO 9001:2000, the organization only needs to be audited against its QMS documentation to determine if the organization is meeting ISO 9001:2000 requirements. Therefore, since the auditor expects the organization to fully comply with its QMS documentation, any instances of noncompliance found during the audit will automatically result in an audit finding. Auditors perform audits in this

ISO 9001:2000 requirements

Documentation audit
(Step1)

Organization's QMS documentation

Auditee interviews
(Step 2)

Auditee

Figure 3.10   How the auditor audits against the ISO 9001:2000 standard.

indirect fashion because auditing an organization to its own procedures is easier for both the auditor and the auditee. The auditor is saved from having to translate each ISO 9001:2000 requirement during the audit interviews into the context of the business and processes of the auditee. This translation is addressed during the documentation audit performed at the start of the registration audit. From the auditee's perspective, questions based on the organization's internal QMS documents are relatively easier to comprehend and answer, as opposed to questions derived directly from a relatively alien document, such as the ISO 9001:2000 standard.

3. *Document change requests.* A mechanism should be available to all employees to request a change to an approved QMS document. A change request form should be available for submission of document change requests. The submitter of a document change request should indicate which document is being requested to be changed, and provide a brief summary of the proposed change along with a reason for the requested change(s). All submitted document change requests should be reviewed periodically by the appropriate PGMs and the quality department, or, minimally, they should be reviewed by the owner of the document and the quality department. Changes accepted for implementation should be implemented within a reasonable time frame. In case a change request is rejected, the request should be formally closed only upon discussion and agreement with the request submitter.

4. *Document change review and approval.* Changes to a previously approved QMS document must be reviewed and approved (as per subclause

4.2.3). Such review and approval should be performed by personnel in the *same roles* as the original reviewers of the document. Note that, since the employees in an organization may be transferred, promoted, or they may leave the organization, it is not advisable to require that changes to documents be reviewed and approved by the *same personnel* who reviewed and approved the previously released version of the document. Some organizations simplify this process of approval of document changes by requiring that only major revisions to a document be approved by all the original approvers. Minor revisions may be approved solely by the author, although such a minor revision should still be provided for review to appropriate parties to preclude a situation where the author performs major changes yet approves the document as a minor revision.

5. *Emergency changes to previously released documents.* A process should be established for handling emergency change(s) to a previously approved QMS document. This process may be occasionally required to immediately rectify critical inaccuracies or deficiencies in an approved QMS document. The emergency change process is intended to be an expeditious yet temporary way of performing a document change, as compared to an organization's standard process for document change that may be more time-consuming. An emergency change process may be as follows:

The submitter of the document change discusses the proposed change with the document's author and quality department. If all parties agree, a hard copy of the document is *redlined* (to indicate the changes), approved, and released for immediate use by the impacted personnel. Immediately thereafter, the author initiates the organization's standard process for implementing the required document change. Following the standard change process, once the document has been formally revised, reviewed, and approved for release, the original redlined copies that were circulated for temporary use are withdrawn and marked obsolete.

6. *Document change identification.* All documents must identify the changes made to them (as per subclause 4.2.3). For this purpose, a change history table as shown in Table 3.5 may be used.

7. *Obsolete documents.* Once a document becomes obsolete, it must be immediately withdrawn from use, or marked "obsolete" to preclude its inadvertent use (as per subclause 4.2.3). If the document is stored in an electronic repository, the document can be electronically tagged as obsolete or withdrawn from the location. If the document has been distributed by means of hard-copy circulation, then each distributed copy of the document must be withdrawn, or somehow physically marked to indicate that it is

Table 3.5 Document change history.

Change History

Document Version	Date	Change Performed By	Summary of Change
Version 1.0	8/1/2002	Wei Hui	First approved release of document
Version 2.0	10/15/2002	Wei Hui	Added new section 4.7 to list product safety requirements
Version 2.1	11/29/2002	Angela Garg	Reformatted Figure 4, and rephrased requirement FNC-08 for clarification.

obsolete. In either case, if the obsolete document has been superseded by a new version, then the new version of the document must be properly distributed (as per subclause 4.2.3).

8. *Document availability.* Mechanisms must be in place to ensure that the correct versions of all applicable documents are easily accessible to the relevant employees (as per subclause 4.2.3). This may be accomplished by providing hard-copy process binders to all the departments, such that the departmental employees can easily access these documents, or by publishing the QMS documents on an intranet Web site. The latter mechanism is increasingly becoming popular due to its sheer ease of use and maintenance. Irrespective of the method used, appropriate employees should be notified upon the release or revision of applicable QMS documents. For this purpose, a periodic notification, say biweekly, is acceptable (unless the change is immediate as a result of an emergency change request).

9. *References and related documents.* QMS documents, when appropriate, should contain a section listing all the documents (and versions, when appropriate) that were either used as a reference while creating the document or are related to the content of the document. This helps point the user to other documents relevant to the subject document.

10. *External release of documents.* Rules governing the external release of QMS documents, such as upon customer request, should be put in place. Acceptable release authorization may include management-level approval from the department that owns the document to be released. Before releasing the document, the owning department should consider purging the document of information that may be deemed confidential, and thus unsuitable for release to an outside party.

11. *Control of documents of external origin.* The organization must ensure that all documents of external origin, such as industry specifications and customer-supplied documents that are used within the scope of the QMS, are clearly identified and their distribution controlled (as per subclause 4.2.3). It is desirable to have a master index of all documents of external origin in the organization along with a reference to each document's location. Such documents may be assigned a document number with a unique identifier to clearly indicate their external origin, such as the use of characters "EX" as the first two characters in the document numbering convention shown in Table 3.4.a.

ENDNOTES

1. This may be any of the following (or equivalent): vice president of quality, director of quality, or manager of quality.
2. Adapted from S.M.A.R.T (specific, measurable, attainable, realistic, tangible) goals from Paul J. Meyer's *Attitude is Everything* (www.topachievement.com/smart.html).
3. Such an implementation team is very similar to the widely known concept of software engineering process group (SEPG). However, SEPGs typically comprise personnel assigned full-time who focus on software process improvement in particular. Therefore, it is perhaps more appropriate to view the ISO 9000 implementation team, which has a wider scope and part-time assignment of personnel, as a work group or task force for implementing ISO 9000. However, such an implementation team could certainly be viewed as the precursor to an eventual SEPG in the organization.
4. The organization chart shown is for illustration purposes only and should not be regarded as a recommendation of a particular type of organization structure.
5. CMMI, *Capability Maturity Model Integration* (CMMI) (Pittsburgh: Software Engineering Institute, Carnegie Mellon University, 2002).
6. Ratikin, S., "Creating Accurate Estimates and Realistic Schedules," *Software Quality Professional* 4, no. 2 (2002).
7. The environment is "like" real-world and not truly real-world because the product is exercised by the customer in its pre-production environment that emulates the operational (or production) environment. At this stage, the product is not yet authorized for actual deployment (use in the production environment), because it is still in development and has not yet achieved the required GA quality criteria.
8. Boehm, B., "A Spiral Model for Software Development and Enhancement," *Computer* 21, no. 5 (1988): 61–72.
9. This quadrant in the spiral model may be executed by "rapid prototyping" or by following the traditional software development process consisting of software design, coding, integration testing, and system testing.

10. This is a general overview and *not* a summary of ISO 9001:2000 requirements related to these subprocesses. ISO 9001:2000 requirements pertaining to these subprocesses are explained in chapters 4 to 8 (under explanation of the relevant clauses).
11. A use-case test entails testing a product against a specific usage scenario by executing a sequence of actions. A use-case test typically exercises several product requirements that pertain to a particular usage scenario. For example, for an automatic teller machine (ATM), one use-case test would be to test whether a customer is able to successfully withdraw money from his account by using the ATM. Note that use-case testing should also be performed during system testing.
12. As an example, refer to *IEEE 730-2002: IEEE Standard for Software Quality Assurance Plans*, or *ISO 10005:1995 Quality Management—Guidelines for Quality Plans*.
13. The implementation planning at this stage is *preliminary* because a significant revision to the implementation plans is usually required upon completion of the preliminary gap analysis due to an improved understanding of what needs to be accomplished.
14. Subsequent gap analyses include: internal quality audits, gap analysis audit(s) performed by the registrar prior to the actual registration audit, and the final gap analysis—which is the registration audit itself.
15. Process ownership should be assigned to the department that has the most significant or majority role in the activities pertaining to a process. Process ownership entails responsibilities for defining the process, implementing the process, monitoring and measuring process execution, and continuously improving the process.
16. Release cycle time may be defined as the time period starting with the initial identification of product requirements and ending with delivery of the finished product to the customer. In other words, it is the duration of a typical software development project in the organization.
17. Subclause 4.2.1 identifies what QMS documentation is required. Further, subclause 4.2.3 contains specific items that must be addressed in the organization's documentation control procedure.
18. This includes all employees in the organization, and not only those involved in the software development process.
19. Sample outlines of two widely used quality manual formats are provided in appendix A.
20. For organizations such as service delivery organizations that do not execute their daily business operations as "project" activities, project documents may be regarded as being equivalent to the usual business documents that the organization produces during daily business operations.
21. Also see explanation of related subclause 7.5.3. As explained in chapter 7, it is desirable that the organization establish one configuration item numbering convention that applies to *all* configuration items, including document identification, software product identification, and so on.
22. There are separate requirements in ISO 9001:2000 governing control of records and these are included in subclause 4.2.4 of the standard.

4

Quality Management System Requirements

At this point you should have sufficient introductory information regarding ISO 9001:2000. This includes familiarity with the structure of the standard and the underlying quality principles; a high-level understanding of the standard's requirements; understanding of the SDLC and the overall context within which the standard's requirements have to be implemented; and information on the implementation strategy. Therefore, you are ready to proceed to the next step: beginning implementation of ISO 9001:2000 requirements.

For successful implementation, one not only needs to understand what each requirement means, but must also understand how to comply with each requirement, such that it can be demonstrated that the intent of the requirement has been adequately addressed. Chapters 4 through 8 provide this guidance. Each requirements clause is explained in the sequence in which it appears in ISO 9001:2000. The explanation of each requirements clause covers the following:

• First, the ISO 9001:2000 requirement is paraphrased to explain *what* specific requirement needs to be complied with. This explanation is *not* intended to be a substitute for the actual ISO 9001:2000 standard but must be used in *conjunction* with an official copy of the standard.

• Second, detailed guidance is provided on *how* to comply with the requirement. Recall that the ISO 9001:2000 standard states what requirements must be complied with, and ISO 90003 provides guidance on application of ISO 9001:2000 in the software industry, but it does not seek to provide detailed "how to" advice for compliance. Providing this second critical piece of information is the key contribution of chapters 4 through 8. The guidance provided is consistent with the interpretation advice contained in ISO 90003.

Note that because most of the requirements clauses contain several requirements, a piecemeal or incremental approach is taken to explain each requirements clause. That is, when appropriate, a requirements clause has been informally decomposed into smaller requirements chunks. The first chunk of requirements under the clause is paraphrased, and implementation guidance is provided on it. Then, the second chunk of requirements under the clause is paraphrased, followed by implementation guidance on it, and so on.

☞ It is worth noting at this point that, as one would expect, organizations find certain clauses of ISO 9001:2000 comparatively more difficult to comply with than others. With the objective of collecting industry information on clauses that were regarded as most difficult to comply with (and to use this information for future improvements to the standard), the U.S. Technical Advisory Group to ISO's TC 176 undertook a product support initiative in 2001. As part of this initiative, a survey to help identify such difficult clauses was developed and provided to organizations that had experience implementing and using ISO 9001:2000. From a survey of 183 organizations, the results of which were reported by Liebesman and Mroz in *Quality Progress* in April 2002,[1] eight clauses that were most frequently reported to be the most difficult to comply with were (in descending order of frequency):

1. Subclause 6.2.2: Competence, awareness, and training

2. Subclause 8.2.1: Customer satisfaction

3. Subclause 8.5.1: Continual improvement

4. Clause 8.4: Analysis of data

5. Subclause 8.5.3: Preventive action

6. Subclause 5.4.1: Quality objectives

7. Subclause 7.3.1: Design and development planning

8. Clause 4.1: General requirements

Further, the survey reported that the top five broad categories against which nonconformances were reported during internal gap analysis (such as, internal audits) and external gap analysis (such as preassessment and registration audit) were:

1. Customer satisfaction data and analysis

2. Documentation

3. Continual improvement

4. Collection and analysis of data

5. Objectives that were not measurable

It can be seen that the areas in which nonconformances were found have a very strong correlation with clauses that organizations find difficult to comply with. Therefore, it is recommended that special attention be paid to the explanation of these problematic requirements clauses in chapters 4 to 8.

CLAUSE 4.1: GENERAL REQUIREMENTS

This clause requires that the organization establish a QMS that is documented, deployed (in use), and continually improved in accordance with applicable requirements in the ISO 9001:2000 standard. In essence, this is a general requirement that can be met by virtue of meeting all the specific underlying requirements that appear in later clauses in the standard. Therefore, the above is to be viewed as an *overarching requirement* which is automatically met if the organization has satisfactorily addressed all *other* requirements in this standard. In other words, no *additional* action is required to meet the aforementioned requirement.

The processes contained in the QMS, along with their sequence, interaction, and permissible exclusions (from clause 7 of the standard) must be clearly identified. Identification of processes in the QMS, along with permissible exclusions, is best accomplished by addressing this in the quality manual (refer to related subclause 4.2.2). It is recommended that the sequence and interaction of the processes be illustrated with the help of process maps, and, additionally, may be explained in the quality manual. This includes processes not only for software product development, but also for supporting operation and maintenance of the product after release to the customer.

All processes must be continually monitored, measured, and analyzed for continual process improvement. Again, this is an overarching requirement that has specific underlying requirements under clause 8 of the standard. Therefore, this requirement can be met by complying with the specific requirements under clause 8 (explained in Chapter 8).

Mechanisms must be in place to ensure effective process execution and control. Necessary action must be taken at all times to ensure that the processes yield desired results. In order to meet these requirements, process owners must ensure that mechanisms to ensure effective process execution and control have been established and built *into* their processes. If appropriate, these mechanisms may be documented in the associated procedures and work instructions. Required corrective and/or preventive actions must be taken to ensure that each process meets its objectives. For example, if a process has been established for system testing, then mechanisms must be established to ensure that the process is effective in meeting its purpose. In this case, the purpose of the process is to validate the product against product requirements. Therefore, the auditor may investigate how the system test personnel ensure that the product has indeed been validated against applicable requirements. If, for instance, the test personnel maintain a document that traces each applicable product requirement to a specific test case, then it would be considered an effective means of ensuring that there is adequate test coverage of product requirements. Similarly, to investigate the control of the system test process, the auditor may investigate if mechanisms are in place for the appropriate management personnel to control system test process execution, or if test personnel are allowed to freely deviate from the established process.

As a general guideline, when identifying needed mechanisms to ensure effective process execution and control, one should ask the following key questions:

- What is the purpose of the process?

- What is the list of criteria to assess the success of the process?

- What controls should be put in place to ensure that the process effectively meets its success criteria?

- What controls must be put in place to control process execution, that is, to keep process execution on track and to minimize process breakdown?

Consider another example—that of peer reviews. The purpose of a peer review is to collect review feedback to improve the overall quality of the artifact being reviewed. The artifact may be project documentation, source code, product documentation, or any such deliverable. A list of acceptable success criteria for a peer review may be as follows:

- Identify maximum possible defects in the artifact.

- Ensure that adequate number of review participants from all relevant areas are present at the review meeting.

- Ensure that all review feedback is adequately addressed in the reworked artifact.

Having identified the success criteria, mechanisms can be established to help achieve them. For example, to maximize defect detection during the review meeting, the moderator should ensure that review participants do not begin discussing problem solutions in the meeting, or use the meeting as a forum for discussing alternative implementation approaches. To ensure that the review meeting has adequate participation, the moderator should be provided the authority to cancel the review if an adequate number of participants is not present. To ensure that the review feedback is adequately addressed, the moderator should be required to perform rework follow-up.

Resources and information required for the execution and monitoring of QMS processes must be provided. Process owners and appropriate management personnel have the responsibility to ensure that all resources necessary for process execution and monitoring are available. A prerequisite for this is that the process owners first identify the resource requirements for executing and monitoring their processes, which should preferably be documented in the associated procedures. When the process is to be applied in a specific software development project, the responsible manager(s) should customize these resource requirements according to the specific requirements of the project and address them in the appropriate planning documents. (Refer to discussion on planning requirements under explanation of clause 7.) Providing required resources and information entails ensuring competent personnel, equipment, and methods are available to execute and monitor processes. Again, considering the example of system testing, the personnel who are testing the product must be competent (as per subclause 6.2.1). They must be adequately qualified and trained to perform their job; they must have appropriate test tools at their disposal (as per clause 6.3); and, they must have required QMS documentation easily accessible to them (as per subclause 4.2.3).

If the organization subcontracts execution of some of the processes within the scope of its QMS, then it must exercise proper control over the supplier(s). Further, the supplier control mechanisms must be identified within the QMS. These requirements are further elaborated upon in clause 7.4. Therefore, detailed guidance on how to comply with this requirement, as well as explanation of what is meant by subcontracted or purchased product in the context of the software industry, is deferred to the explanation of clause 7.4.

CLAUSE 4.2: DOCUMENTATION REQUIREMENTS

Subclause 4.2.1: General

This subclause requires that the organization document its quality policy, quality objectives, quality manual, documented procedures and records specifically required by ISO 9001:2000, and documents required by the organization to effectively plan, execute, and control its processes. Note the following:

- Detailed discussion on the establishment of the quality policy and quality objectives is addressed later in the explanation of related clause 5.3 and subclause 5.4.1.

- This subclause defers requirements pertaining to the quality manual to subclause 4.2.2.

- The complete list of procedures and records required by ISO 9001:2000 was provided earlier in Table 2.1.

- Guidance on creating QMS documents required by the organization to ensure effective process planning, control and execution was discussed in "Documentation Strategy" in chapter 3.

- This subclause defers requirements pertaining to records to subclause 4.2.4.

Subclause 4.2.2: Quality manual

This subclause requires that a quality manual be established and maintained and it minimally include the following information: scope of the QMS and permissible exclusions, along with supporting rationale; mention or reference to the documented procedures for the QMS; and an explanation of the interaction of the processes in the QMS.

Guidance on the establishment and maintenance of the quality manual was provided earlier in chapter 3.

Subclause 4.2.3: Control of documents

This subclause requires the establishment of effective mechanisms for document control. This covers the following items: document approval, document changes, availability of documents at points of use, document identification, control of documents of external origin, and proper disposition of obsolete documents.

Guidance on control of documents was provided earlier in chapter 3.

Subclause 4.2.4: Control of records

This subclause requires that records be maintained to demonstrate that the implemented QMS is effective and conforms to ISO 9001:2000 requirements. It must be ensured that all records are legible, clearly identifiable, and stored in an accessible location. Further, this subclause requires that all aspects pertaining to control of records, such as identification, storage, protection from unauthorized access and disasters, ease of accessibility, duration for retention, and eventual disposition, must be addressed in a documented procedure.

Before studying these requirements, it is necessary to understand what a record is. A record is evidence of an activity performed or results achieved. Records are not only required for external use—to demonstrate conformance to ISO 9001:2000 to the organization's registrar and customers; they are also required for internal use. Internal reasons to maintain records include the need for the records in assessing whether required tasks have been performed and for use as input for business decisions.

At the time the QMS processes are first being defined, adequate thought should be given to what records need to be maintained for each process and who would be responsible for creating them. This includes records that are specifically required by ISO 9001:2000 (refer to Table 2.1, page 19). The respective record producers and their management personnel have the responsibility to ensure that the records produced are legible, clearly identifiable, and provided for storage at the appropriate locations. However, for some critical records, it may desirable to have this independently verified. For example, the quality department may be required to review and approve all product test records.

All records should be maintained in secure yet easily accessible location(s). A centralized location for storage of most QMS records is preferred as opposed to dispersed locations. Records may be maintained in both hardcopy and electronic format. The responsibility for physically storing a record should also be identified; it may reside with the record producer, or there may be a dedicated record controller who verifies all records prior to storage in an approved location. Consideration should also be given to who should be allowed to access a particular record. Controls should be put in place to prevent the records from being compromised, or corrupted by computer viruses (in the case of electronic records), or accessed by unauthorized personnel. Unless a record is confidential in nature, access to the records should be generally available. Consideration should also be given to securing the records from a disaster, such as natural calamities. In the case of electronic records, this can be done relatively easily with a periodic backup of the storage systems. If a record is stored on electronic storage media, consideration should be given to the rate at which the respective storage media degrades, thus possibly compromising integrity of the record. Consideration should also be given to whether the organization continues to have the appropriate tools to access records stored on media that has become obsolete, or is quickly becoming obsolete.

For each record, the retention time and disposition state must be identified. The disposition state of a record determines how the record is handled after its retention time has expired. For example, a record may be physically discarded at the end of its retention period, or it may be moved to an archival location for an even longer or indefinite period. From an auditing perspective, a record that is past its retention time is generally considered nonauditable for the purpose of verifying its correctness and completeness, even though it may be stored in an archival location.

ENDNOTE

1. Liebesman, S., and J. Mroz, "ISO 9001: 2000 Experiences: First Results Are In," *Quality Progress* (April 2002).

5

Management Responsibility Requirements

The previous chapter explained requirements belonging to clause 4 of the standard—a clause that contains overarching and fundamental requirements pertaining to the subsequent clauses. The general requirements in clause 4 provide a broad outline of a QMS infrastructure, while the documentation requirements deal with the foundation of any ISO 9000 implementation—QMS documentation. With fundamental elements of the QMS in place, one can begin addressing the first essential prerequisite for an effective QMS—management commitment. Clause 5 of the standard contains specific requirements which, if met by an organization's senior management, serve as ample proof of senior management involvement in and commitment to quality and continuous improvement.

CLAUSE 5.1: MANAGEMENT COMMITMENT

This clause requires that senior management visibly demonstrate its commitment to the establishment and continual improvement of the QMS by communicating to employees the importance of meeting customer and regulatory requirements. Senior management is also responsible for establishing the quality policy, and must ensure that quality objectives are established. Senior management must conduct periodic management reviews of the organization's QMS, and must ensure availability of sufficient resources for the execution of QMS processes.

In order to meet this requirement, first it must be ensured that senior management commitment has been secured. If an organization is pursuing an ISO 9000 registration but management commitment appears to be lacking, then the management representative has the unenviable challenge of selling quality to senior management. Fortunately, there are approaches that can be used to accomplish this task. First, it should be realized that the senior management in any organization is keenly interested in the satisfaction of its key stakeholders—customers, shareholders, and employees. Therefore, it is best to sell the benefits of quality management and improvement to senior management by demonstrating with the help of factual data how each of these stakeholders would benefit. For example, senior management may be provided documentation on how much money and time is lost due to poor quality (commonly referred to as *cost of poor quality*), which in turn hurts the organization's bottom line and the impression given to its shareholders. Similarly, senior management may be educated on how lack of adequate quality assurance and quality control activities directly impacts the quality of the product and services delivered, and thus negatively impacts customer satisfaction. They may also be educated regarding the unfavorable impact of inadequate employee training and unclear allocation of responsibilities on employee satisfaction. Senior management may also be informed of the success stories from other organizations that have focused on quality and have seen their continuous quality improvement efforts result in increased customer satisfaction levels. For example, many organizations with sound QMSs perform and report on periodic customer satisfaction surveys to track the impact of their quality improvements on customer satisfaction levels.

Once senior management commitment to quality has been secured, the organization can demonstrate compliance to the requirements in this clause in many different ways. Senior management must communicate to employees the importance of meeting customer expectations and statutory and regulatory requirements. Such communication may take place at employee all-hands meetings, or other organizational get-togethers. Documented records of such communication are not required. The ISO 9000 auditor(s) may interview the employees to determine if such communication from senior management has occurred.

Senior management must ensure that it regularly reviews the state of the QMS in accordance with requirements under clause 5.6. Senior management must establish a quality policy in accordance with requirements in clause 5.3, and must ensure that quality objectives have been established in accordance with requirements in subclause 5.4.1. It must also ensure that needed[1] resources to execute QMS processes and deliver quality products are made available to appropriate employees. The ISO 9000 auditor(s) may interview the employees to inquire about the resources they need to perform their tasks, and determine if needed resources were indeed provided in a timely fashion. Any deficiencies found in resource provision may be reported as an audit finding[2] against senior management. Similarly, lack of an organizational quality policy or lack of quality objectives would be reported as an audit finding against senior management.

CLAUSE 5.2: CUSTOMER FOCUS

This clause requires senior management to ensure that customer requirements have been adequately determined and met with the objective of improving customer satisfaction. This requirement is supplemented by subclauses 7.2.1 and 8.2.1 of the standard that contain specific requirements pertaining to determination of product requirements and measurement of customer satisfaction.

In essence, this requirement exists primarily to *emphasize* that, ultimately, it is the responsibility of senior management to ensure that customer's requirements, stated and unstated, have been adequately determined and met. In order to meet this requirement, senior management must ensure that *processes* for the determination of customer requirements and measurement of customer satisfaction have been established as per subclauses 7.2.1 and 8.2.1. In the case of contract-based companies, senior management must ensure that product requirements are identified and formally agreed upon between the customer and the organization. In the case of product-based companies, senior management must ensure that the product requirements are identified and formally agreed upon between the requirements authoring department and the product development department.

In both the aforementioned scenarios, this clause states that senior management must ensure that all product requirements agreed to with the customer are satisfactorily met. To satisfy this requirement, senior management must ensure that *mechanisms* exist in the organization to validate the product prior to release in order to confirm that all product requirements have indeed been met. Acceptable mechanisms for this include: availability of a validation report or records that demonstrate that the product has been validated to the documented requirements, and records of a formal meeting that was held to review the product against product release criteria. In case of any deviations from the documented requirements, these should be handled as per clause 8.3 of the standard.

CLAUSE 5.3: QUALITY POLICY

This clause requires senior management to establish a quality policy that is relevant to the organization, and reflects the organization's underlying quality philosophy and commitment to continual improvement.

In order to comply with this requirement, it must be ensured that the defined quality policy is commensurate with the business of the organization. The established quality policy must be appropriate for the organization, or else it will be alien and meaningless to the employees, and therefore, is unlikely to be adhered to. For example, a developer of mission-critical software for space exploration may emphasize *reliability and achievement of zero defects* in its quality policy, while a developer of telecommunication network switching software may emphasize *robustness and fault tolerance* in its quality policy. While defining the quality policy, it is best to think of key quality attributes that are critical to the success of the organization and its products and then formulate the quality policy such that it communicates the organization's focus on the key quality attributes and its commitment to continuous improvement.

Most organizations prefer establishing a concise quality policy, typically no longer than a few sentences (refer to the Sanmina-SCI Company quality policy sidebar), while some organizations have been known to establish a quality policy that generally runs a few pages and provides a high-level description of the organizational commitment to quality and the infrastructure in place to achieve it.

This clause also requires that the quality policy be communicated throughout the organization. Possible ways of communicating the quality policy include:

- Posting the quality policy in strategic places throughout the organization

- Including the quality policy in the quality manual that is distributed to all employees

- Stating the quality policy on the organization's coffee mugs distributed to all employees

- Explaining the quality policy in QMS training

- Quizzing employees about the quality policy in internal quality audits

Note that inquiring about the awareness and understanding of the quality policy among the employees, and assessing whether the quality policy has truly been implemented, is a popular area of investigation for most ISO 9000 auditors.

Finally, senior management must ensure that the quality policy is periodically reviewed for its continued appropriateness. Typically, because the

---

SANMINA-SCI QUALITY POLICY STATEMENT[3]

"Sanmina-SCI is focused to deliver excellence in performance, flexibility and technology to exceed customer expectations in quality, delivery, and service.
These goals are achieved through strategies that focus on:

- Exceptional customer service

- Global consistency

- Web-based systems that provide effective communication and real-time trend analysis

- Employee empowerment and development

- Most advanced technologies available in the industry

- Internal and external benchmarking."

---

quality policy is intended to be a general high-level statement of organizational commitment to quality and continual improvement, organizations word their quality policy in such a fashion that it is not specific to time and instead is so worded that it continues to be relevant and applicable over an extended period of time. This is perfectly acceptable and, in fact, desirable since it prevents problems associated with having to withdraw and revise the previously documented quality policy, and promulgate the revised quality policy to employees and customers (with little gains, if any). However, senior management must ensure that the quality policy is reviewed periodically for its continued relevance and revised, if necessary. Such periodic review may be performed annually or after a significant corporate restructuring, merger, or acquisition. Bear in mind that the quality policy should not be used for documenting near-term quality goals and objectives; these should be separately documented as discussed later in explanation of subclause 5.4.1.

CLAUSE 5.4: PLANNING

Subclause 5.4.1: Quality objectives

This subclause requires senior management to ensure that quality objectives have been established across the organization, both for the QMS as well as for the product. The established quality objectives must be measurable, that is, they should meet the SMART criteria explained earlier, and they must not be contrary to the organization's quality policy.

Quality objectives for the QMS are now explained, followed by an explanation of quality objectives for the product.

When establishing quality objectives for the QMS, both long-term and short-term objectives should be formulated. As an example, long-term quality objectives may[4] pertain to a two- to five-year time horizon, while short-term quality objectives may extend from the present time to the next one to two years. Initially, quality objectives are qualitatively formulated, and then they are gradually decomposed, elaborated, and quantified to yield SMART objectives. The definition of short-term quality objectives of an organization entails a careful breakdown of the organization's long-term quality objectives into feasible short-term annual targets. For example, an organization may begin the formulation of a long-term quality objective by stating that it plans to significantly reduce software defects. In order to quantify this objective, it first needs to determine its current software defect density. Say it currently produces three software defects per thousand lines of source code (KLOC), that is, three defects/KLOC, and over a five-year period it plans to reduce this software defect density to no more than 0.5 defects/KLOC. Therefore, proposing to "reduce software defect density to 0.5/KLOC at the end of the next five years" may be a valid long-term quality objective. However, in order to ensure that this long-term objective is met, it should target achieving this goal in smaller increments by setting short-term quality objectives, such that progress toward the long-term objective can be continually monitored and corrective action taken in a timely fashion. In this case, proposing a "reduction in software defect density by 0.5 annually over the next two years" may be a valid short-term quality objective. Clearly, if the organization is able to achieve its short-term quality objectives it will provide a high degree of assurance that it is on the right path and its long-term quality objective is achievable. However, if it encounters significant difficulty in achieving these short-term quality objectives, then it knows that it needs to either revise its plan of action or redefine the quality objective if it is deemed to be unsuitable.

The described example illustrates how long-term and short-term quality objectives may be closely related, and, in essence, that long-term objectives are implemented by adopting a phased approach using short-term objectives. Consider a second example: an organization may choose to keep the long-term and short-term quality objectives relatively separate wherein the long-term quality objectives are primarily qualitative and strategic in nature, while the short-term quality objectives are SMART and tactical in nature. For example, the long-term quality objectives may be to improve product time-to-market, reduce product defect rates, and improve productivity. However, in the near-term, the organization may have only two objectives:

to achieve ISO 9000 registration by a specified date, and to achieve improvement in customer satisfaction level to a specific level by a specified date. Once the short-term quality objectives have been met, the organization can start tackling the formerly long-term quality objectives by elaborating and quantifying them.

In both examples, the short-term quality objectives should always be SMART, and once these have been defined, they should be supported by specific improvement actions that will be undertaken to achieve identified objectives. Identification of the improvement actions should be coordinated by the person who has been assigned the quality objective and is minimally a management-level employee. The responsible person should solicit input from other relevant employees in the organization. Without such a list of agreed improvement actions, achievement of the short-term quality objective is likely to be jeopardized. If the individuals who are responsible for implementing the improvement do not have a clear understanding of what needs to be done in order to achieve the quality objectives, then chaos and disjoint efforts will result. As an example, if the short-term quality objective is to reduce software defect density by 0.5 over the next year, then the list of improvement actions may include:

- Provide software developers training on effective code review techniques in order to increase the defect detection efficiency during code reviews.

- Identify new test tools to automate the unit test process.

- Introduce causal analysis and defect prevention techniques to analyze each reported software defect.

Once a list of supporting improvement actions is available, they should be formally documented in an improvement action plan (refer to Table 5.1) and approved by appropriate personnel prior to implementation. Implementation progress should be reported at the periodic management reviews of the QMS.

The most challenging aspect of establishing SMART quality objectives is *how* to arrive at such SMART objectives. A detailed discussion on different approaches to formulate SMART objectives is beyond the scope of this book, but be aware that there are two essential elements of any possible approach:

- First, the current state (and measurement) of the quality attribute to be improved must be known. For example, before specifying a quantitative goal for improving software defect density, current measurement data on software defect density must be obtained.

Table 5.1 Example of a SMART quality objective and supporting improvement action plan.

Improvement Action Plan		
Reference ID: Qual-Obj-2003-01		
Quality objective: To improve the average customer satisfaction rating for "quality of customer service" from current level of 6.5/10 to 7.5/10 by the time of the next annual customer satisfaction survey in 2004.		
Responsible: Mike Morris Vice-President, Customer Service	Approved by: David Shier Management Representative	
Improvement Actions	**Responsible**	**Due Date**
1. Initiate quarterly meetings with key customers to discuss customer satisfaction issues.	Kathy Malone	March 31, 2003
2. Provide product and process training to all customer service personnel.	Mary Davis	June 16, 2003
3. Implement metrics-driven process improvements in the customer service department.	David Curry and David Shier	May 1, 2003

• Second, when formulating a quality objective, special attention must be paid to ensure that a proposed objective is acceptable and realistic. This can only be achieved by formulating objectives *collectively* with the appropriate process owners and management personnel, as opposed to being dictated to them.

Once quality objectives have been identified, they should be approved by senior management to ensure that they are consistent with management's vision of the QMS. It is recommended that at the time of annual performance review of employees, the activities listed in the improvement action plan(s) for the QMS quality objective(s) be tied to the individual objectives of the relevant employees for the following year. For example, an action plan item, such as "Identify new test tools to automate the unit test process" may be recorded as an individual objective for the software development manager by the manager's supervisor. The software development manager may in turn decompose the higher-level objective into lower-level objectives to be assigned to his or her staff. For example, one staff member may be assigned the objective to research and recommend candidate COTS unit test tools that meet the stated need; and a second staff member may be assigned the objective to perform a comparison study of the candidate tools. Such a cascading down of quality objectives across different levels in the organization enables the organization to tie its improvement objectives to individual employee objectives, in turn maximizing probability of success because the employees are aware that their incentives and rewards are contingent upon them successfully achieving their identified objectives.

In addition to ensuring the establishment of QMS quality objectives, senior management must also ensure that qualitative and quantitative product quality objectives are established. In essence, product quality objectives constitute the quality criteria against which a product is to be assessed prior to release. As an example, product quality objectives may include criteria to confirm that:

- The product has been verified for compliance with the specified product requirements.

- Product does not contain defects beyond the permissible number (and severity) of defects in a released product.

- All supporting documentation for the product is available and has been reviewed.

- Mechanisms are in place to support the product after release.

In order to facilitate achievement of product quality objectives by timely corrective and preventive action, *intermediate* quality objectives should be established for use across all functions and levels of the organization. In other words, quality objectives should be specified for use *during* the product development process as entry and exit criteria for handoff between departments. For example, consider the product quality objective that requires confirmation that the product has been verified for compliance with the specified product requirements. To ensure that this quality objective is indeed satisfied during the product test process, it should be listed under the exit criteria for the product test process. That is, the product test process should not be considered complete until this requirement has been met. Similarly, in order to ensure that the output from the product development department is acceptable to the product test department, the product test department may specify as an entry criteria that it requires records from the product development department describing the results of product verification activities performed by that department. It is important to realize that product quality objectives can only be met by making quality pervasive throughout the organization. An organization that only establishes final product quality objectives and does not establish intermediate quality objectives will most likely fail in meeting its product quality objectives.

Subclause 5.4.2: Quality management system planning

This subclause requires that senior management ensure that the QMS is planned such that all QMS requirements included in clause 4.1 of the standard are satisfactorily addressed.

In order to adequately meet this requirement, it is recommended that QMS implementation planning be performed as per the implementation strategy outlined in chapter 3. Items that should be addressed in QMS implementation planning include, but are not limited to:

- Performing high-level process mapping

- Identifying lifecycle model(s)[5] available for use

- Identifying required artifacts during product development, such as project plan(s), SRS, SDD, software code, user documentation, and so on

- Establishing expected content for the required documents by means of templates

- Establishing supporting methods, such as unit test guidelines, software coding standard, and so on

At this time, consideration should also be given to providing guidance on how the organization's SPDP and supporting methods may be tailored for projects. Though formal methods for tailoring a standard software process exist,[6] for most organizations, an informal process tailoring approach is generally sufficient. This entails the author of the project quality plan requesting all departments involved in the project to provide information on the requested deviations from the SPDP, along with supporting rationale. The proposed deviations are then documented in the project quality plan and reviewed and approved as part of the review and approval of the project quality plan.

Senior management must ensure that adequate planning is performed in order to facilitate the achievement of the identified quality objectives. For the achievement of *QMS* quality objectives, senior management should ensure that associated improvement action plans, or similar documents, exist. For the achievement of *product* quality objectives, senior management should ensure that project planning documents, such as project plan(s), product test plan(s), project quality plan, and similar documents exist to describe what quality activities will be performed during the project.

This subclause also requires that senior management ensure that the integrity of the QMS is maintained when changes to the QMS are implemented. One possible way to meet this requirement is to establish a detailed traceability matrix to trace each ISO 9001:2000 requirement to the QMS. Since the quality manual is the highest-level description of the QMS, it is preferable to include such a traceability matrix in the quality manual. The primary benefit of such a traceability matrix is that it serves as a valuable tool to ensure that all the requirements of the standard have been addressed in the

QMS. A secondary benefit is that it serves as an excellent tool for ensuring continued compliance to ISO 9001:2000 requirements in the event of a change to the QMS. An example of such a traceability matrix is shown in Table 5.2. For each clause and subclause of the standard, the matrix identifies the QMS element (not necessarily documented) that serves as evidence to demonstrate compliance with the associated ISO 9001:2000 requirement. Along with each QMS element, the responsible department is also identified.

Table 5.2 ISO 9001:2000 to QMS traceability matrix (partially completed).

ISO 9001:2000 Clause	ISO 9001:2000 Requirement	QMS Element	Process/ Document Owner	Compliance (Acceptable/ NA*)
4.1	General requirements	Quality manual	Quality department	Acceptable
		Product development process map	Quality department	Acceptable
		All QMS procedures	Various	Acceptable
		Supplier management procedure	Procurement department	Acceptable
4.2.1	General	Quality policy	Quality department	Acceptable
		Long-term and short-term quality objectives	Various	Acceptable
		Quality manual	Quality department	Acceptable
		QMS procedures and records	Various	Acceptable
4.2.2	Quality manual	Quality manual	Quality department	Acceptable
4.2.3	Control of documents	Documentation and record control procedure	Documentation department	Acceptable
4.2.4	Control of records	Documentation and record control procedure	Documentation department	Acceptable

* As per subclause 4.2.2, for any clauses marked as NA (not applicable), the justification for nonapplicability must be included in the quality manual. Note that such permissible exclusions are limited to requirements in clause 7 only. Because this is a partial table for illustration purposes only, clause 7 requirements do not appear in it.

As an example, clause 4.1—"General requirements" is collectively addressed by the QMS elements—quality manual, product development process map, all QMS procedures, and the supplier management procedure. Therefore, if the organization plans to revise any of these QMS elements, it must ensure that the requirements contained in clause 4.1 of the standard (and other clauses, if applicable) continue to be met after the revisions.

CLAUSE 5.5: RESPONSIBILITY, AUTHORITY AND COMMUNICATION

Subclause 5.5.1: Responsibility and authority

It is the responsibility of senior management to ensure that organizational responsibilities and authorities have been defined and communicated.

In order to meet this requirement, senior management should ensure that an overall organization chart and departmental organization charts have been established. A high-level organization chart that explains the scope of the organization's ISO 9001:2000 registration should be included in the quality manual (refer to Figure 3.1, page 34). Also, a high-level summary of the key responsibilities of each department that is in scope of the ISO 9001:2000 registration should be provided in the quality manual (refer to appendix A).

In addition to this high-level summary of departmental responsibilities, position descriptions should be established for each role in the organization. Position descriptions should list the responsibilities and competency requirements associated with each role (refer to explanation of clause 6.2). The list of departmental responsibilities documented in the quality manual complemented by the position responsibilities documented in the position descriptions help effectively define all the responsibilities and authorities in the organization. Employees should be aware of the general responsibilities of other departments, minimally of those departments that they are required to interact with as part of their jobs. This helps ensure that departments that interact have a consistent understanding of each other's responsibilities, and it helps preclude situations where quality falls through the cracks due to misunderstandings regarding who is supposed to do what.

Subclause 5.5.2: Management representative

This subclause requires senior management to appoint a member of management to serve as the management representative, with the responsibility of establishing and maintaining the QMS, reporting to senior management on the performance and needed improvements to the QMS, and promoting awareness of customer requirements.

An explanation of desirable qualities of a management representative and a description of associated responsibilities was provided in chapter 3.

Subclause 5.5.3: Internal communication

This subclause requires senior management to ensure that communication mechanisms are established, and effectiveness of the QMS is communicated to all employees.

These requirements can be met by following the guidance on communication mechanisms provided in chapter 3. Note that mechanisms described in chapter 3 (or similar mechanisms) should also be used for sharing appropriate information on effectiveness of the QMS with all employees. Such information on effectiveness of the QMS includes, but is not limited to, customer satisfaction data, measurement data, and results of internal and external quality audits (refer to related clause 8).

CLAUSE 5.6: MANAGEMENT REVIEW

Subclause 5.6.1: General

Senior management must periodically review the QMS to monitor its adequacy and effectiveness, and to identify opportunities for improvement. Deficiencies or needed changes in the QMS must be investigated for appropriate corrective and preventive action.

In order to meet this requirement, the management representative should first establish the membership of the management review team. Membership of the management review team should typically be limited to senior management and the management representative only. Management review meetings should be chaired by the management representative. They should be run as per a formal agenda that should be supplied in advance to the meeting participants along with the presentation material. Management reviews should have an established quorum, that is, the minimum required attendance for a meeting to be held. Discussion on corrective and preventive action is deferred to chapter 8.

The quality policy and quality objectives must be reviewed for their continued suitability, and revised if necessary.

Note that discussion on suitability (and maintenance) of the quality policy and quality objectives was included in explanation of clause 5.3 and subclause 5.4.1 respectively.

This subclause also requires maintenance of records of such management reviews in accordance with requirements of subclause 4.2.4. Subclause 5.6.3 further clarifies what are minimum required outputs from such management reviews.

Subclause 5.6.2: Review input

This subclause specifies what items must be used as input to management reviews so that the objectives of such reviews can be effectively achieved. These items include:

- Review of open action items from past management reviews

- Results of external and internal quality audits (refer to related subclause 8.2.2)

- Customer feedback and customer satisfaction data (refer to related subclause 8.2.1)

- Quantitative data (measurement trends) and qualitative information regarding process performance and product conformity (refer to related subclauses 8.2.3 and 8.2.4)

- Status of corrective actions, preventive actions, and improvement actions currently in implementation

- Planned changes that may affect the QMS

- Recommendations for improvement of the QMS

If the organization subcontracts some of the processes within the scope of its QMS, then supplier-related quality issues should also be input to the management review. These include status of requested corrective, preventive, and improvement actions; results of supplier audit(s); quantitative and qualitative data regarding the supplier's process performance; and conformity of the subcontracted product to requirements.

Subclause 5.6.3: Review output

This subclause states that the output of management reviews must include, but is not limited to, decisions and action items pertaining to improvement in effectiveness of the QMS, improvement in product conformity to customer requirements, and resource requirements.

In order to comply with this requirement, formal minutes of meetings describing the meeting discussions, decisions, and assigned action items must be maintained. These, along with the meeting presentation material, should be regarded as records and controlled as per subclause 4.2.4.

ENDNOTES

1. Identification of needed resources is discussed in the explanation of clauses 4.1 and 6.1.
2. The terms "audit finding" and "nonconformance" are used interchangeably in the industry and in this book.
3. Reproduced with permission from Sanmina-SCI Corporation.
4. Short-term and long-term time periods vary from one organization to the other and depend on factors such as an organization's release cycle-time period.
5. Because an organization may undertake different types of projects and/or develop multiple products, it is acceptable to have more than one lifecycle model in use. However, when more than one lifecycle model is available for use, criteria should be established to provide guidance regarding which lifecycle model is suitable for use in what context or project. For example, a spiral lifecycle model may be preferable for the purpose of rapid prototyping of a new product, as opposed to a waterfall lifecycle model.
6. Nanda, V., "On Tailoring an Organizational Standard Software Development Process for Specific Projects," In *Proceedings of the 11th International Conference on Software Quality*, Pittsburgh, 2001.

6

Resource Management Requirements

This chapter explains all resource management–related requirements that are contained in clause 6 of the standard. Examples of resources include, but are not limited to: personnel, IT infrastructure, physical work environment, information, and financial resources. As explained in the previous chapter, it is the responsibility of senior management to provide the needed resources. These requirements are now examined in detail.

CLAUSE 6.1: PROVISION OF RESOURCES

This clause requires the organization to determine and provide necessary resources to implement, maintain, and improve the QMS, and to enhance customer satisfaction.

In order to meet this requirement, resources required to implement the QMS must first be identified, and then provided. Resource planning for QMS implementation should be performed as per guidance provided in chapter 3. This entails an initial determination of planned activities, followed by an initial estimate of required resources for the same. The initial identification of needed resources can then be further refined as the plans are further elaborated.

In addition to resources required for QMS implementation, resources must be determined and provided for the maintenance and improvement of the QMS, and for the enhancement of customer satisfaction. This entails providing resources for:

- Maintenance-related activities, such as maintenance of the QMS documentation; auditing the QMS; and ongoing measurements collection and trends analysis

- Improvement-related activities, such as implementation of corrective and preventive actions; actions resulting from quality audits; and actions based on collected process and product measurements

- Activities essential for enhancing customer satisfaction, such as actions required on the basis of customer satisfaction surveys, actions required to respond to customer complaints, and product verification and validation activities to ensure that customer requirements have been met

The responsibility to identify resource needs for these activities lies with the responsible employees and department management personnel, while the responsibility to ensure that needed resources are provided in a timely fashion belongs to senior management. Since resource needs are pervasive throughout the QMS, identification and provision of resources should be addressed in appropriate QMS procedures and work instructions. That is, if there is a documented procedure to describe process "A" and there is another documented procedure to describe process "B," then the resource requirements for each of these processes should be addressed in their respective procedures.

CLAUSE 6.2 HUMAN RESOURCES

Subclause 6.2.1: General

This subclause requires that employees whose work directly or indirectly impacts product quality must have adequate competency level. Explanation of these requirements is deferred to subclause 6.2.2.

Subclause 6.2.2: Competence, awareness and training

This subclause requires that competency needs be identified for employees whose work affects product quality, and these be addressed by means of training (or equivalent actions).

☞ Note that this requirement applies only to employees whose work directly or indirectly affects product quality; this *includes* contract personnel as well. While it is desirable to identify and address competency need for employees working in accounting, sales, marketing, finance, and so on, it is not specifically required by this subclause.

In order to comply with this requirement, it is first necessary to understand what competency is. Competency is the demonstrated ability to apply knowledge and skills and it is derived from education, training, skills, and experience. Skills may include both technical and soft skills. Technical skills, as the name suggests, pertain to technical skill requirements to perform the job, while soft skills pertain to behavior, attitude, communication, and leadership requirements to perform the job. Competency needs of different employees in the same role may be different because different employees possess different competencies. Consequently, the gap (competency needs) between what they need to know to perform their job (competency requirements), and what they already know, will vary. Therefore, to determine the competency needs of an employee, the job competency requirements must be known. Competency requirements need to be determined not only to identify training needs for employees, but also for use as criteria in hiring of new employees, and to determine eligibility for promotion of current employees. Specification of competency requirements also enables the organization to determine the extent of documentation required for the associated QMS processes. Recall that subclause 4.2.1 cites the *competence of personnel* as one of the criteria that should be considered when deciding how much QMS documentation is required.

The determination of competency requirements for a position should be made by the supervisor for that position. When identifying competency requirements, it is important to keep in mind that competency requirements need not necessarily be identified for each position (or role) in the organization. Instead, competency requirements may be identified for a family of similar positions, such as department managers and directors. It is recommended that competency requirements be identified in an employee job description, as depicted in Table 6.1. Table 6.1 lists the job responsibilities as well as required and desired competencies. Desired competencies are "nice to have" though not critical to the job. They may be used during employee hiring to distinguish between two otherwise equally capable candidates. Once an employee has been hired, desired competency-related training might be imparted to the employee for ongoing professional development of the employee. However, an employee not having any of the desired competencies does not render the employee "unqualified" to perform his or her job. On the other hand, if an employee is lacking required competencies, then the employee is considered unqualified to perform his or her job and this deficiency must be immediately rectified by providing the employee with the required skills.

Table 6.1 Sample job description (including competency requirements).

Job Description

Job title: Software Quality Assurance Engineer

Department: Quality Assurance	**Reports to:** Manager, Quality Assurance

Summary:
This employee is responsible for performing quality assurance tasks for software products.

Responsibilities:
- Establish, maintain, and continually improve ABC Corporation's QMS
- Perform and/or participate in software quality assurance tasks for software products, such as quality planning, peer reviews, and measurements collection and analysis
- Perform internal quality audits
- Represent the quality department at project review and management meetings
- Conduct employee training on the QMS

Required Competencies:

Experience:
- 2–5 years in software quality assurance

Technical Skills:
- Proficient in all phases of software development
- Understanding of quality systems relating to software development
- Sound understanding of ISO 9000

Soft Skills:
- Strong interpersonal and communication skills

Education:
- Bachelor of science degree in computer science (or equivalent)

Desired Competencies:

Technical Skills:
- Experience in use of other quality maturity models, for example, CMMI
- Previous position as a software developer and/or system test engineer
- Exposure to Unix, and C or C++ programming languages

Education:
- Master's of science degree in computer science (or equivalent)

Certification:
- Professional certifications as quality engineer, quality auditor, and so on

Once competency requirements have been identified, the determination of employee competency needs can be initiated. There are primarily two sources for the identification of employee competency needs:

- Competency needs identified at the time of hiring of a new employee, or promotion/transfer of an employee into a new position

- Competency needs identified during the course of everyday process execution

In order to determine employee competency needs at the time of hire or at the time of promotion or transfer of the employee, the employee's supervisor should meet with the employee to determine the employee's current competencies. The employee's current competencies can then be compared with the job competency requirements to yield the *gap* in required competencies, that is, competency needs. Similarly, competency needs may be determined during the course of everyday process execution. For example, deficiencies in employee competencies may surface during quality audits; a change in a process may result in need for retraining employees; a breakdown in process execution attributed to human failure may result in need for retraining employees; and annual performance reviews of employees may lead to the identification of new training needs.

Once competency needs have been identified, they should be documented in an employee competency gap matrix, as shown in Table 6.2. New competency needs should be added to the matrix as and when they are identified, and competency needs once addressed should be marked as completed. New competency needs may arise due to the employee being asked to work on a special assignment that requires a particular competency; or the employee's job responsibilities change (in which case the employee's job description should also be enhanced to list the new required competencies); or the new competency is required for use of a new technique or tool; or the employee is to be groomed for another position that requires the new competency.

Competency needs, once identified, must be addressed by training or by other actions such as outsourcing of certain processes, modification of processes, and/or modification of QMS documentation. Quite often training is inappropriately used as the first solution to deal with a competency gap, when in fact a modification of the process and its supporting documentation may be more appropriate. Therefore, all viable options should be investigated instead of assuming training will rectify all competency-related deficiencies.

Once competency needs have been addressed, effectiveness of the actions taken must be assessed to help identify areas of improvement. Effectiveness may be defined as the extent to which planned objectives are met. There are different ways to determine the effectiveness of the actions taken:

• *Student testing.* A commonly used technique to assess training effectiveness entails administering the same test to the students prior to and at the end of the training, and comparing the two test scores to determine the extent to which the students have learned from the training. The assessment of training effectiveness should not be confused with training evaluation. Although the two overlap in certain areas, they have distinct objectives.

Table 6.2 Employee competency gap matrix.

Competency Gap Matrix for System Test Department

Employee Name: Novice Testman   **Title:** Junior System Tester   **Level (select one):**
Manager ☐ Team Leader ☐ Test Engineer ☑

#	Training Name	Training Method[1]	Complete?	Vendor[2]	Completion Criteria[3]	Due Date	Completion Date
Technical skills							
1	Remedy—Defect management tool	CBT	☑	Internal	Quiz	7/18/03	07/14/03
2	System test process	Self-study	☑	Internal	Quiz	6/27/03	6/27/03
3	Quality system overview	WBT	☑	Internal	Quiz	2/4/03	2/18/03
Soft skills							
4	Building highly effective teams	ILT	☐	Teamwork Inc.	Certificate	9/26/03	
Certifications							
	None						

1. Computer-based training (CBT), instructor lead training (ILT), Web-based training (WBT), self study, on-the-job training (OJT), mentoring

2. Internal, external (specify company name)

3. Quiz, course exam, NA

Training evaluation involves collection of student *satisfaction feedback* on the course content, delivery method, instructor evaluation, and training facility. On the other hand, assessment of training effectiveness entails testing of the students to determine whether and how well the students have *learned* the training content material.

• *Quality audits.* By definition, quality audits are performed to determine compliance with applicable quality requirements, and to determine adequacy and effectiveness of the QMS. Therefore, they serve as an excellent means to assess the effectiveness of any actions taken to satisfy employee competency needs. Because quality audits entail auditee interviews, examination of documents and records, and observation of activities, they provide ample opportunities to the auditor to identify deficiencies in employee competence.

• *Measurements program.* Use of measurements can serve as yet another means to determine the effectiveness of actions taken. Use of appropriate measures before and after the actions are taken can help provide evidence of improvement in employee competence. For example, if some employees attended a training course on "peer review techniques," then one can reasonably expect to see an overall increase in the number and severity of defects recorded for future peer reviews.

• *Employee satisfaction survey.* An employee satisfaction survey provides valuable information from employees regarding their personal satisfaction with the training provided to them, or the effectiveness of actions taken pertaining to their area of work. For example, if QMS documentation pertaining to customer service employees was created or significantly revised to address employee competence needs, yet in the employee satisfaction survey customer service employees indicate that QMS documentation is lacking or inadequate for them to effectively perform their job, then it indicates an area for further corrective action.

This subclause also requires that employees be aware of the relevance and importance of their activities in the overall organizational product development (or service delivery) process, and be aware of their contribution in meeting defined quality objectives.

In order to promote employee awareness regarding where and how they contribute in the overall organizational process, the organizational process map serves as an excellent starting point. It enables the various departments to visibly identify themselves in the overall organizational process. The underlying QMS documentation helps further elaborate the relevance and contribution of each of the departments and its employees. Therefore, it must be ensured that the employees have been appropriately trained on the applicable QMS documentation. For promoting employee awareness regarding how he or she contributes to the achievement of the overall quality objectives, each employee must be made aware of:

- Practices that help achieve the defined quality objectives, for example:

  - Planning by the employee for assigned tasks by means of appropriate documentation, such as project plan(s), test plan(s), and development plan(s)

  - Faithful execution of the defined processes by each employee

  - Employee's review of his or her own output prior to handoff to the internal or external customer

- How the employee's improvement actions tie in to the overall quality objectives. This can be accomplished by means of an improvement action plan that identifies the employee's improvement action(s) associated with a higher-level quality objective (refer to Table 5.1 and accompanying explanation).

Finally, this subclause requires the maintenance of employee competency records, that is, records of employee education, training, skills, and experience. In order to meet this requirement, it is recommended that a separate competency records file be maintained for each employee. This file should be considered nonconfidential, that is, it must be open to examination by internal and external quality auditors. Therefore, it should be maintained separately from confidential employee information, such as salary and benefits information. Copies of the employee's education records, originals or copies of employee training certificates, competency gap matrix, and other pertinent records should be filed. Also, when training is performed by in-house training instructors, then records of the competence of the training instructors should also be maintained.

CLAUSE 6.3 INFRASTRUCTURE

☞   Similar to the next clause, clause 6.4, this clause is quite subjective in nature, in that there is a greater possibility of disagreement between the organization and its registrar. However, there are recommended steps an organization should follow to demonstrate that it has carefully read these requirements and made the best possible attempt at compliance. An organization would be found to be noncompliant with clauses 6.3 and 6.4 only if it has completely ignored these clauses, or blatantly violated the spirit of these requirements in its implementation.

This clause requires the organization to determine, provide, and maintain the infrastructure needed to comply with product requirements. ISO 9000:2000 defines infrastructure as a system of facilities, equipment, and services needed for the operation of an organization.

In order to comply with this requirement, the first step is to determine the required infrastructure, for example:

- Facilities and workspace equipment

- Hardware equipment (such as desktops, laptops, servers, and routers)

- Software tools:

  - Design, development, and support tools, such as compilers and software test tools

  - Tools required for the organization's IT infrastructure, such as antivirus software, network software, and firewall software

  - Development, test, and support environments

  - Software libraries

- Communication technology equipment

- Transportation

- Packaging material

Infrastructure requirements may be documented in the appropriate procedures as well as project-specific plans. For example, software test tools to be used in a specific project should be specified in the associated project planning documents. Specification of key infrastructure requirements for a project in the associated project planning documents enables the organization to have a record of items that need to be made available. Further, prior to acquiring a software tool for use (whether in-house or third-party), an evaluation should be performed to determine if the tool would meet organizational needs (refer to explanation of subclause 7.3.6). Also, procured software tools should be placed under configuration management control (refer to explanation of subclause 7.5.3). Finally, bear in mind that ISO 9001:2000 does not require that all infrastructure requirements be documented. Therefore, care should be exercised to document only those infrastructure requirements that the organization deems appropriate.

CLAUSE 6.4 WORK ENVIRONMENT

This clause requires the organization to determine and manage the work environment necessary to comply with product requirements.

ISO 9000:2000 defines work environment as a set of conditions under which the work is performed. These conditions may include physical, social, and environmental factors, such as temperature, recognition programs, and ergonomics. In order to comply with this requirement, the organization must first determine which work environment–related factors are critical for it to meet product requirements. Due consideration should be given to work environment factors, such as cleanliness, safety, lighting, protective equipment, pollution, heat, humidity, and employee recognition programs. Again, the auditor will observe whether the organization has paid due consideration to the requirements in this clause or has summarily ignored them due to their somewhat subjective nature. Poor upkeep of the workspace would be easy to point out as an audit finding; reasonable upkeep, not necessarily immaculate, would be deemed acceptable.

7

Product Realization Requirements

M ost of the requirements of ISO 9001:2000 are contained in clause 7 of the standard. This is also the only clause of the standard against which permissible exclusions are allowed, provided that such exclusions do not impair the organization's ability to meet applicable requirements or otherwise prevent it from adequately discharging its responsibilities. This clause contains requirements covering all aspects of planning for product realization, product requirements, design, development, purchasing (and subcontracting), control of production and service provisioning, and control of monitoring and measuring devices. These requirements are explained next.

CLAUSE 7.1: PLANNING OF PRODUCT REALIZATION

This clause requires that the *processes for* product realization be *planned and developed*. This requirement can be met by planning and tracking the development of product realization processes in accordance with the detailed guidance provided in chapter 3. This clause also requires that all planning activities for product realization be performed in accordance with applicable QMS processes. For example, if an organization is beginning work on a project and a standard QMS process for project planning exists, then the standard process must be followed when planning for the project.

When planning the product realization processes, the organization is required to determine:

Product Quality Objectives

Establishment of product quality objectives was discussed earlier under explanation of subclause 5.4.1.

Product Requirements

Product requirements must be determined in accordance with subclause 7.2.1 of the standard.

Required Processes, Documents, and Resources

The organization must identify the processes, documents, and resources it will need for producing the product. Typically, the SPDP and its subprocesses, including description of required resources, and templates and forms for documents are established as *standardized* QMS documentation. This means that each instance of developing a product or its subsequent enhancements is required to adhere to the applicable QMS documentation. The need to tailor standardized QMS documentation for a specific project[1] should be addressed by means of quality planning. The output of quality planning may be a stand-alone project quality plan,[2] or the information may be distributed in several documents, such as a software development plan, system test plan, and so on. Information contained in such a project quality plan may include but is not limited to:

- Purpose and scope of the project quality plan

- References to related project planning documents

- References to relevant QMS documentation (such as software coding standard, unit test guidelines) applicable to the project

- Specification of, or reference to, quality requirements applicable to the product

- Specification of, or reference to, applicable product release criteria

- Specification of, or reference to, how failures to comply with any release criteria are to be handled

- Specification of, or reference to, entry and exit criteria for each project phase

- List of planned verification, validation, monitoring, inspection, and test activities

- List of project metrics

- List of deviations[3] (from the QMS documentation) for this specific project

In order to understand this concept of tailoring, consider the following example: An organization requires its products to be formally reviewed as per a specified inspection process, and the results recorded in an inspection record. In this case, the inspection process should be documented in an inspection procedure, which should also describe resource needs for performing inspections. The documented inspection procedure should be published as an approved QMS document along with the form for the inspection record. Say a specific project necessitates minor changes to the standard inspection process or has unique resource needs, such as the procurement of a new type of inspection tool. If these are one-time deviations from the standard QMS documentation, then these *temporary* deviations (from the defined procedure) for the specific project should be listed in the appropriate project planning documents. However, if these deviations pertain to a *permanent* process change, then the appropriate QMS documentation must be revised.

Finally, in the case of software being developed for a limited purpose, such as a throwaway prototype, quality planning need only be to the extent to verify that such software is relatively error-free and fit for its intended use.

Required Verification, Validation, Monitoring, Inspection, Test Activities, and Acceptance Criteria

In order to meet the verification requirement, the organization must establish appropriate verification mechanisms to ensure that the output of each phase in the SDLC complies with the input for that phase (or in other words, follows the blueprint from the previous phase). Simply put, verification is done to make sure you have done the *thing right*.[4] Reviews, both formal and informal, serve as one such mechanism for performing such verification activity. For example, a key objective of the software design review is to ensure that the design is complete, in that it addresses all applicable requirements documented in the SRS, which constitutes the input to the design phase. Similarly, the output of the coding phase (software code) must comply with the software design document that constitutes the input for that phase. Other verification mechanisms include demonstration by prototyping, testing, simulation, and analysis.

Similarly, the validation requirement can be met by establishing mechanisms to validate that the product does indeed comply with product requirements. Typically, this validation is provided by a system test of the product, where the product is tested by running a suite of system test cases that are traced to the product requirements. For product requirements that may not be appropriate for validation by system test, such as requirements for the creation of customer training material related to the product, a review of the customer training material may be performed to validate that the applicable requirements have been met.

This clause also requires that the organization identify monitoring activities for product realization. This requirement is best met by embedding the monitoring mechanisms in the respective processes. It should be recognized that while the responsibility to monitor overall project status rests with the project manager, the responsibility to monitor interdepartmental issues rests with the respective department managers and the project manager, and the responsibility to monitor intradepartmental issues rests with the respective department manager. For example, the project manager may schedule a weekly meeting as a mechanism to monitor the overall status of the project, and take timely corrective and/or preventive action when necessary. Similarly, the system test manager may monitor the weekly rate of discovery of new problems during system test, to assess whether the quality of the product is gradually beginning to improve. Ideally, the rate of defect discovery during a project should resemble a Rayleigh curve, as shown in Figure 7.1. In fact, such measurement data can be extrapolated, by means of specific computations, to project when the product is likely to be

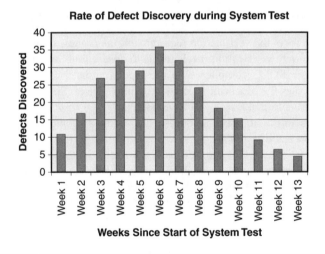

Figure 7.1   Rate of defect discovery during system test (Raleigh Curve).

ready for release. (Further discussion is beyond the scope of this book. Refer to Conte et al.[5])

Required reviews[6] in the SPDP must also be identified. This requirement can be met by stipulating what type of review is required for each artifact in the SPDP, and when such reviews should be performed. For example, one organization may require that all project documents be inspected; another may require a predefined set of key documents to be inspected, while other artifacts may be informally reviewed. An informal review may be a private review by one reviewer or a collective review involving several reviewers. Informal reviews lack the formality associated with inspections. For example, a review record for an informal review may not be mandatory, and if one is created, it generally does not require an independent follow-up by the moderator after the review to verify that each review remark has been addressed. An informal review may also take the form of a walk-through meeting where the author walks the reviewers through the artifact, and provides real-time explanation of the content while inviting comments on observed defects. Inspections, generally in the form of Fagan-style inspections,[7] when performed, must be performed prior to the approval of the document (as per subclause 4.2.3), and at appropriate stages in the SDLC, that is, prior to the end of the associated phase in the SDLC (as per subclause 7.3.4). It is preferable to establish guidelines or checklists to guide the conduct of the various reviews. Such guidelines or checklists, when established, should be customized for each type of artifact review for which they are to be used. For example, a software design review checklist would differ from a code review checklist. On the other hand, an organization may choose not to establish review-specific guidelines, and instead may only specify a set of general review guidelines that are applicable to all reviews. Specific requirements pertaining to reviews are covered under the explanation of the related subclause 7.3.4.

The organization must also specify what test activities are to be performed during the SDLC. This requirement can be met by identifying required software test activities, such as unit testing, integration testing, and system testing (including testing of product documentation). It should be ensured that there is consistency in the understanding of the test personnel regarding what type of tests they are responsible for, where in the SDLC each type of test is to be performed, and the purpose and methodology for each type of testing. Although ISO 9001:2000 does not mandate that this be documented in a procedure, it is certainly desirable to do so to promote a consistent understanding within the organization. Specific requirements pertaining to testing are covered under the explanation of related subclause 7.3.6.

This clause also requires that the criteria for product acceptance be established. Typically, in the case of contract-based companies, this requirement is met by having acceptance test criteria contractually agreed to between the organization and its customer. Upon release of the product to the customer, the customer undertakes the execution of acceptance testing of the product in the customer's operational environment to ascertain whether the product complies with the previously agreed acceptance test criteria. Product-based companies, on the other hand, adopt one or more of the following options in establishing acceptance criteria:

1. Similar to contract-based companies, they may establish acceptance test criteria in consultation with key customers.

2. They may establish acceptance test criteria, which instead of being agreed to with customers, are agreed to with the product manager, who is the internal customer for the software development organization. Successful execution of such acceptance test cases, which typically are business *use-cases* to exercise the system and are run after successful completion of system testing, is the basis for the authorization of product release. Successful completion of acceptance testing may be used in conjunction with a third option that is described next.

3. There may be internally determined acceptance criteria that are agreed to with the product manager and the quality department. Typically, such acceptance criteria take the form of *release criteria* against which the product is to be assessed prior to release. The product is authorized for release if all criteria are met, and in case of unsatisfied criteria, the risks associated with them have been mitigated, or are otherwise deemed acceptable. Release criteria may be established early in a project, at the time of the creation of the project's quality plan, or it may be a standardized set of criteria applicable across various projects. When standardized release criteria exist, they should be tailored, as needed, in the respective project plans to indicate what, if any, deviations apply to a specific project. By their very nature, such release criteria are wider in scope than the traditional acceptance test criteria. Such release criteria generally address but are not limited to:

- Confirmation that the product contains all the functionality as specified in the PRD

- Confirmation of completion of system testing and acceptance testing (if applicable) activities and achievement of the associated test exit criteria

- Confirmation of the availability of the product on the appropriate media, such as compact disc (CD)

- Readiness of product documentation for the product

- Readiness of training material for the product

- Confirmation that the technical support organization has the required software environment, installed product software, and expertise to handle and troubleshoot customer calls after the release of the product

- Confirmation that there are no contractual issues that need to be addressed before release of the product, and so on

Required Records

Appropriate records must be available to demonstrate that the product meets product requirements, and the processes meet ISO 9001:2000 and internal QMS requirements (as specified in the organization's QMS documentation). Control of records must be exercised in accordance with subclause 4.2.4.

In order to comply with this requirement, the organization must specify what records are required to be created during the SPDP. To determine what records are required to be created, the following criteria should be used:

1. Request appropriate records that will provide evidence that the executed processes meet ISO 9001:2000 and internal QMS requirements. As an example, if the system integration procedure requires that a suite of system integration tests be executed to verify that the product has been successfully integrated and is ready for system test, then evidence in the form of test logs and/or a test report (or equivalent documentation) must be maintained. This will enable an auditor to subsequently verify that indeed the system integration tests were successful.

2. Request appropriate records that will provide evidence that the final product meets requirements. For example, records of system testing and records of formal review of the product against acceptance criteria provide evidence of the conformance (or nonconformance) of the product to requirements.

3. Request records that are explicitly required by ISO 9001:2000 (refer to Table 2.1 in Chapter 2 for the complete list of records required by ISO 9001:2000).

Finally, this clause re-emphasizes what is already stated in subclause 4.2.1 and explained earlier in this book—that the output of the planning of product realization must be in a form that is appropriate considering the organization's size, complexity of processes, nature of business, and other such factors.

CLAUSE 7.2: CUSTOMER-RELATED PROCESSES

Subclause 7.2.1: Determination of requirements related to the product

This subclause requires that the organization determine all requirements pertaining to the product. This includes: requirements specified by the customer for delivery and post-delivery; requirements not specified by the customer but essential to support the known use of the product; applicable statutory and regulatory requirements; and any supplementary requirements identified by the organization.

As explained earlier, in the case of contract-based companies, the complete set of product (and support) requirements is typically specified by the customer. Or, they may be documented by the supplier and then approved by the customer, or they may be jointly developed. In the case of product-based companies, however, requirements are internally identified and approved by taking into account the current and future needs of customers. In other words, the requirements are internally generated but externally driven. In both cases, as well as in the case where software is being developed in-house solely for the purpose of supporting internal business processes of the organization, a method for agreement on the requirements and for the authorization and tracking of subsequent changes should be established. That is, it should be clearly identifiable and known who formally approves the requirements, who may authorize changes, and how requirement changes are identified. For example, in the case of a product-based organization, the requirements document (including subsequent changes) may be formally approved by the product manager and the appropriate management authority in the software development organization. In the case of requirement changes, the change history table may be used to reference the specific requirement that has been added, deleted, or modified. In the case of contract-based companies, a change in key requirements may necessitate a contract amendment. The requirements are documented in a PRD and SRS(s), templates of which are presented in appendix B.

When prototypes or demonstrations are used to help refine requirements for the software to be developed, there should be an established method that specifies who assesses the prototype or demonstration and how this feeds into the requirements definition process. Typically, the prototype or demonstration is shown to the customer (internal or external) who uses it as an input to further refine the requirements. Records of such informal requirements reviews and meetings should be maintained, as appropriate, so that there is an adequate audit trail to explain why and upon whose request a particular requirement was added, deleted, or modified. Note that such records may be in the form of meeting minutes, archives of e-mail exchanges, or other suitable means.

It should be ensured that the organization authoring the requirements and the development organization are consistent in their understanding of key terms pertaining to the requirements, and the meaning and purpose of each requirement. While the former can be achieved by formally defining key terms and sharing a common terminology guide, the latter should be addressed during requirements reviews by being alert to requirements ambiguity and providing additional clarification in the requirements documents, as appropriate.

It should also be ensured that each requirement is traceable to the final product. This can be achieved by implementing appropriate traceability matrices throughout the SDLC (refer to explanation of related subclause 7.5.3).

During the requirements definition process, the organization must also ensure that all implied requirements are determined. These are those requirements that are not explicitly stated but necessary in order to support the implementation of the requirements that are explicitly stated. Such implied requirements should be documented in the appropriate requirements documents so that the designers have the complete set of requirements that need to be designed into the system. Also, applicable statutory and regulatory requirements must be specified. In some instances, these may be explicitly stated by a customer, or they may be implied by virtue of the organization intending to sell the product in a particular market that has unique statutory and regulatory requirements. Generally, such statutory and regulatory requirements are safety and emissions requirements applicable to electronic assemblies, for example, CE, FCC, UL, and so on. However, some countries, such as China, impose their own statutory and regulatory requirements on software systems (such as telecom software), which must be met before the product can be certified for sale in the country.

Finally, this subclause requires that the organization determine any additional requirements. This includes ancillary requirements, such as training requirements, that may require existing product training material, if any, to be enhanced to reflect the new functionality incorporated into the product. When COTS software needs to be procured, requirements for the COTS software must be identified in accordance with subclause 7.4.2.

Subclause 7.2.2: Review of requirements related to the product

This subclause states that prior to committing to supply a product, an organization must review the product requirements. During the requirements review, it must be verified that the requirements are well-defined, unambiguous, and the organization's understanding of them is consistent with that of the customer. Further, the organization must have the ability to meet the requirements. The same must be verified in the event of changes to previously approved requirements (or contract). When the organization discovers a discrepancy in the documented requirements, from what may have previously been agreed, the discrepancy must be resolved with the customer.

In order to comply with this requirement, following is a sample list of issues that should be considered during requirements and contract reviews:

1. Ensure that the requirements are achievable within the parameters of schedule, cost, and resources (including technical ability of resources to meet the requirements).

2. Ensure that the contractual agreement accurately reflects the current and/or planned features and capabilities of the product so as not to preclude the satisfaction of any contractually agreed items.

3. Ensure that each requirement can be validated to confirm it was met.

4. Ensure that the requirements are complete and there are no missing requirements.

5. Agree on a mechanism for identifying and mitigating requirements-related risks. This includes technical risks, resource risks, schedule risks, and so on.

6. If a product is being built to contract, and periodic joint reviews of project progress are required, clarify when such reviews will take place, or the mechanism for scheduling such joint reviews.

7. Confirm standards, or specific processes, that are required to be used during the SDLC, for example, software coding standard.

8. Clarify use of third-party software or customer-supplied items, if any. This should include criteria for the acceptability of customer-supplied items, and a mechanism for handling those deemed unsuitable for use.

9. Review responsibilities of the customer under the contract, including provision of customer-supplied items, as agreed to with the organization.

10. Clarify hardware requirements and operating system requirements, including patch levels (if appropriate).

11. Agree on control of external product interfaces. For example, the customer may mandate that the existing product application programming interfaces (APIs) not be changed.

12. Confirm delivery requirements, including alpha and beta deliveries, if any.

13. Clarify organization's responsibility pertaining to third-party software incorporated into the product by the organization.

14. Ensure appropriate nondisclosure agreements are in place to protect the intellectual property of the organization and the customer.

15. Agree on requirements pertaining to safekeeping of a true copy of the product in an escrow location (for use in the event of a disaster).

16. Communicate warranties associated with the product.

17. Confirm the duration of support requested by the customer (standard support or extended support).

18. If the customer has requested to perform quality audit(s) of the organization, agree upon when, where, and how such audits may be scheduled and performed.

This subclause also requires that records of requirements and contract reviews be maintained. Typically, in the case of requirements document reviews, organizations perform an inspection, and an inspection record is created. However, in the case of contract reviews, minutes of meetings with a list of action items and their disposition are acceptable.

In cases where a customer supplies no documented requirements, the organization must ensure that customer requirements are confirmed before they are accepted. In essence, an organization would be found to be non-compliant with this requirement if it is unable to demonstrate to the auditor that it indeed confirmed the customer's requirements before accepting them. Note that confirmation here does not necessarily mean written agreement. Depending upon the scope of the task, such confirmation may have been obtained by exchange of correspondence (including electronic), a meeting with the customer (with appropriate records), and so on.

Finally, in the event of changes to previously approved requirements, the appropriate requirements document(s) must be revised. Such revisions to requirements document(s) should be approved by personnel in the same roles that approved the previous version of the requirements. All personnel that are impacted by the requirements change must be notified immediately so that the child documents, such as design documents, can be updated accordingly.

Subclause 7.2.3: Customer communication

This subclause requires that the organization identify and deploy effective mechanisms for communicating with the customer. Customer communications must address product information, inquiries, contracts (including amendments), customer feedback, and complaints.

First, it should be recognized that communication with customers is an ongoing activity. Customer communication commences when an organization first approaches a prospective customer. It then takes the form of contractual negotiations and agreement; keeping the customer informed during the product development process; and, finally, technical support after product release. As the engagement with the customer progresses through various stages in this meta-process (described earlier), there are various departments in the organization that come to the forefront with the responsibility of communicating with the customer. At the front end prior to contractual negotiations, typically the sales and marketing departments are the primary interface. During contractual negotiations, contracts and legal personnel are the primary interface. During product development, the product manager or project manager typically act as the primary interface. After product release, the customer service department becomes the primary interface for communicating with the customer.

From an ISO 9001:2000 perspective, the standard is interested in customer communication mechanisms beginning with contractual negotiations. Provisions should be made to review and rework the draft contract with the customer until it is satisfactory in terms of clarity of content and acceptability of terms. Appropriate personnel should be utilized to furnish information requested by the customer, and to assist in contract reviews and discussions, as appropriate. The same is true in the event of a contract amendment.

Once the contract is approved and product development is under way, depending on whether it is a product-based company or a contract-based company, communication obligations to the customer may vary, and they should be handled accordingly. For product-based companies, customer communications may be limited to informing the customer whether progress is on track to achieve previously communicated product release date(s), and involving key customers in design partner forums to collect customer input for design of the product. If early releases of the product are to be provided to the customer, as under a formal alpha or beta program, then extensive communication may be required to release these interim versions of the product. This may cover setting customer expectations regarding the early release program, collecting product feedback from the customer, and agreeing on priorities for what customer reported defects are critically required to be fixed in the GA release of the product. In the case of contract-based companies, the customer is typically intimately involved in periodic review of overall project progress, participation in milestone reviews, and review of project plans, requirements documents, design documents, prototypes, and test reports.

At the time of product release, the customer needs to be provided information on use of the product in the form of product documentation and online help, as appropriate. The customer should also be provided information[8] such as:

- New features included in the product

- Known defects in the product (including late-breaking news inserts on defects discovered very close to product release)

- Defects in previously released versions of the product that have now been fixed

- Information on hardware and operating system versions (including patch levels) the product is certified to work with

Beyond product release, mechanisms should be in place to capture and track customer calls, for example, by deploying COTS software for customer relationship management. Mechanisms must be established to collect customer satisfaction information from the customer (as per subclause 8.2.1), and to keep customers informed on the current status of their requests, such as change requests, requested defect fixes, and customer complaints. As appropriate, information should be shared with customers on planned product changes and new features, and anticipated impact to customers of these planned changes.

CLAUSE 7.3: DESIGN AND DEVELOPMENT

Subclause 7.3.1: Design and development planning

This subclause requires that the design and development of a *product* be planned and controlled. In planning for the design and development of a product, the organization must determine the design and development stages, required review, verification and validation activities, and the associated authorities and responsibilities.

In order to comply with this requirement, it should first be recognized that the planning and control of the design and development of the product has to be in accordance with the organization's established SPDP. In other words, the project plans have to be based on approved QMS documentation, and tailored from them, as appropriate. Note that this QMS documentation must have been created in compliance with clause 7.1 requirements.

☞ Note the subtle difference between clauses 7.1 and this subclause. Clause 7.1 talks about planning and developing the *processes for* product realization, while this subclause talks about planning and control *for a specific product (or project)* in accordance with the established processes.

To ensure consistency in planning for product realization across projects, there should be an established process for project planning. A standardized template for a project plan or a software development plan should exist, and it should cover items such as[9]:

- Purpose and scope of the project

- Specification of the software baseline on which the development is to begin

- Identification of key project team members from each department, and allocation of responsibilities for the project

- Estimation for the project, including:

  - *Resource requirements.* Cost (including labor, travel, and material cost); personnel; and required hardware and software tools and environments. In case of subcontracted software, criteria for the acceptability of the subcontracted software should be established, and planning should address verification of the subcontracted software for acceptability. Planning should also address requirements specification for the subcontractor, and agreement on cost and schedules.

– *Key milestone dates and detailed project schedule.* In creating the schedule, a detailed work breakdown structure for the project should be created, and a critical-path analysis should be performed.

Estimates should be based on historical data from similar projects, and when appropriate, should be derived using a structured estimation technique, such as the Wideband Delphi Method for project estimation.[10] Appropriate amount of contingency should be included in the estimates. The basis of estimates should be documented so it can be explained how each estimate was arrived at. For example, if a design document is expected to require 60 person-hours to be created, then the basis of estimate may be recorded as follows:

– *Preparation of design document.* (Using the 80 percent rule, that is, assume an employee performs only 32 person-hours productive work in a 40-hour work week):

  * 60 person-hours/32 person-hours = 1.875 person-weeks (75 person-hours)

  * Add 10 percent for contingency, that is, 75 + 7.5 = 82.5 person-hours (final estimate)

- Reference other project planning documents, such as project quality plan, configuration management plan, integration plan, migration (porting) plan, and test plans

- Development process for the project, including planned project phases and activities in each phase

- Customer and supplier (or subcontractor) involvement during the project, such as joint reviews and approvals

- Assumptions and dependencies associated with the project

- Initial identification of project risks, and risk mitigations and contingencies

- Employee training needs due to unique project requirements

- Post-mortem analysis of the project

This subclause also states that the interfaces between the various departments must be managed so that each department has a clear understanding of its responsibilities and those of other departments. In order to comply with this requirement, identification of the role of each department and allocation of responsibilities should be addressed in the associated QMS documentation. Also, in addition to identifying key project team members and allocating responsibilities in the project plan, the project plan should specify what project-specific reviews will be scheduled, and when, to review progress and facilitate communications across departments.

Finally, this subclause states that the planning documentation must be updated, as appropriate, during project execution. In order to comply with this requirement, there should be regular reviews of project progress against plans. If needed, the original estimates and plans for subsequent project phases should be updated at the end of each project phase. This is because, as a project progresses, the amount, depth, and quality of information the project team possesses about the project consistently improves. Therefore, the knowledge acquired should be used to replan the project, when necessary, to perform real-time management of project progress against realistic plans.

Subclause 7.3.2: Design and development inputs

This subclause requires that the inputs to product requirements be determined and records maintained.

Product requirements can originate from various sources (refer to related subclause 7.2.1). Therefore, in order to define a requirement set that is complete, it is important to consider all possible sources during requirements definition. Keep in mind that awareness of the input for a requirement also helps provide the justification for why it exists. This helps weed out requirements that were neither requested nor implied, or otherwise necessary, and thus represent a scope creep from what is required in the product. Sources of requirements that should be considered during the requirements definition process include, but are not limited to:

- Functional and nonfunctional requirements that are explicitly requested

- Requirements identified due to the design constraints imposed on the system

- Requirements implied in order to achieve another stated requirement (such a requirement may also be derived from experience with a similar design in the past)

- Requirements necessary due to statutory and regulatory considerations

- Requirements necessary to address approved change requests against the product

- Requirements necessary to satisfy customer-specified acceptance criteria

This subclause also requires that the input to product requirements be reviewed for adequacy. As stated earlier, requirements should undergo cross-functional review with appropriate participants, and during the review, it must be ensured that all explicit and implicit requirements have been identified. Reviewers must verify that stated requirements are complete, accurate, unambiguous, possible to validate, consistent, and achievable.

Subclause 7.3.3: Design and development outputs

This subclause requires that the output from the design and development phases be in such a form that it is possible to verify the outputs of these phases against the inputs for each of these phases.

Design output is typically in the form of a formal design document, such as the SDD, and if needed, a design document for the product documentation. The SDD should illustrate how the software will be designed to satisfy the requirements contained in the SRS. (Refer to the SDD template in appendix B.) The design document for the product documentation, if created, should illustrate how the product documentation will be structured, and it should provide an overview of each user manual. Development output is typically in the form of product source code and accompanying product documentation. Development output must be verified against design output in accordance with subclause 7.3.5.

This subclause states that design and development output must be approved prior to release. In the case of design output, it is recommended that such approval be formal, such as by signature approval on the subject document. In the case of development output, such as software code, a more informal mechanism, such as authorization from the appropriate software development management personnel prior to initiation of the software build activity, is sufficient.

This subclause also states that when the design or development output is to be used for purchasing, or for production or service provisioning, it must contain appropriate information for those purposes. For example, if a product is intended to include a subsystem from a subcontractor, then the design of the product must illustrate where and how the subcontracted subsystem fits in the resulting product, and what the interfaces are with the subcontracted subsystem.

This subclause also states that design and development outputs must contain or reference product acceptance criteria. To avoid redundancy, it is recommended that only a reference be provided to the product acceptance criteria (refer to discussion on product acceptance criteria under explanation of clause 7.1). Acceptance criteria should also be established for each intermediate product in the SDLC. This provides assurance that the outputs of each stage comply with the inputs for that stage. In essence, intermediate acceptance criteria are a list of prerequisites, the achievement of which is *essential* to proceed any further in the process with minimal risk. For this purpose, exit criteria should be established for each stage in the SDLC, and a review or verification activity should be performed at the end of each phase to verify satisfaction of the exit criteria. When necessary, appropriate corrective action should be taken. For example, the acceptance criteria for the end of the analysis phase in the SDLC may be specified as, "All SRSs must be complete and formally approved." Prior to obtaining approval of the SRSs, they must be reviewed. Once all remarks made at the requirements review have been successfully addressed, the SRSs can be approved.

Tools intended for use in the SDLC should also be validated prior to use. This validation should be performed in accordance with subclause 7.3.6 and/or clause 7.6.

Finally, this subclause requires that characteristics of the product that are essential to its safe and proper use must be specified. This requirement can be addressed by being mindful of such characteristics of the product during the SDLC, and by ensuring during reviews, verification, and validation activities that these characteristics are adequately specified. For example, during product documentation reviews, reviewers should ensure that product characteristics that are essential for its safe and proper use are stated and appropriately highlighted to the user, for example, with the use of special icons.

Subclause 7.3.4: Design and development review

This subclause states that at appropriate stages in the SDLC, design and development of the product must be reviewed in accordance with established plans. The review must entail an evaluation of whether the design and development complies with requirements, and when necessary, appropriate corrective action must be taken.

To comply with this requirement, the organization must perform design and development reviews according to established plans for the product (refer to discussion on design and development planning under

explanation of subclause 7.3.1). In defining the review process, consideration should be given to items such as:

- How is each type of review (formal or informal) to be conducted?

- What roles are required for a review (for example, reviewer, moderator, recorder, author)?

- What are the responsibilities of each role (before, during, and after a review)?

- How are review participants selected? Note that this subclause specifically states that participants must include representatives from areas who have a vested interest in a specific review.

- What preparation is required prior to a review?

- What are the acceptance criteria for a review to be considered successful?

- What review records must be created?

- What document and records management activities need to be performed once the review is complete?

This subclause also states that review records must be created, along with
a record of how the actions from the review were handled. To comply with this
requirement, it must be ensured that the reviewed artifact is not approved
until all requested actions in the review record have been completed, and
risks associated with open actions have been identified, accepted, and appropriate actions have been taken to monitor and mitigate them. One way of
ensuring this is by requiring that the author of the artifact respond to each
requested action in the review record by indicating whether the action was
completed, and provide a reason if the action was not completed as
requested. Note that ISO 90003 further recommends that a procedure be
documented to describe how deficiencies and nonconformities identified at
such reviews are to be handled (refer to related clause 8.3).

Subclause 7.3.5: Design and development verification

This subclause states that at appropriate stages in the SDLC, the design and
development outputs must be verified in accordance with established plans.
The verification must entail an evaluation of whether the design and development complies with requirements, and when necessary, appropriate corrective action must be taken.

In order to comply with this requirement, the organization must perform verification activities in accordance with the established plans for the

product (refer to subclause 7.3.1). When the results of the verification indicate that the output does not comply with the input for that phase, then appropriate corrective action must be undertaken, and the verification activity repeated (as per clause 8.3). For example, if the design review uncovers significant flaws in component design, then the component should be redesigned and the design documentation rereviewed. However, in the case of minor defects in the design, where there is agreement between the reviewers on what correction is required, it may be sufficient for the moderator to verify that the design has been reworked, without need for an additional review. The organization should preclude use of unverified or incorrect artifacts by requiring that only verified and approved design and development artifacts be placed under an approved configuration management baseline. If some issues remain unresolved, risks associated with them should be identified, accepted, and mitigated by appropriate actions.

This subclause also requires that the records of verification and of actions taken be maintained. For this purpose, verifications records, such as software design review records, code review records, and unit test reports, must be controlled (in accordance with subclause 4.2.4). In this case, evidence must be available to demonstrate that actions requested at such reviews and defects reported in the unit test reports were properly handled.

Subclause 7.3.6: Design and development validation

This subclause states that design and development of the product must be validated in accordance with established plans. Validation must entail an evaluation of whether the design and development complies with requirements, and when possible, validation must be performed prior to release of the product.

To comply with this requirement, the organization must perform validation activities in accordance with the established plans for the product (refer to subclause 7.3.1). When the results of the validation indicate that the output does not comply with the stated product requirements, then appropriate corrective action must be undertaken, and the validation activity repeated.[11] As stated previously in chapter 3, in order to simulate the operational scenario of the customer, the product should be validated by conducting system tests in an environment similar to the real world. When it is not feasible to mimic the real-world environment or to validate a specific use of the product, then all such test limitations should be clarified up front and risks associated with these limitations should be identified and mitigated. For example, if certain requirements cannot be tested due to an acceptable reason, then a code review may provide a form of validation. When such alternate means to validate the requirements are contemplated, they should be commensurate with the criticality of the requirement and risks associated with possible failure. For example, in the case of source code for critical safety elements of shuttle software, it would be unacceptable to limit the validation to a code review, when people's lives are at stake. When such validation limitations are accepted, they should be documented in the system test plan, along with the associated risk and risk mitigation. They should be reviewed and agreed upon with the customer, as appropriate, to ensure that they are acceptable to the customer.

Validation can be performed by conducting testing at various levels of software aggregation, and during different stages in the SDLC. For example, black-box unit testing of individual software components constitutes one form of validation testing and so does integration testing of aggregation of software components.

When planning for each type of test, the objectives and scope of the test effort should be clarified, test resource requirements and responsibility for testing should be specified, and entry and exit criteria for each test phase should be clearly specified. Test planning should address types of tests that are to be conducted. For example, types of tests that may be performed during system test include installation tests, configuration tests, functional tests, user-interface tests, usability tests, use-case tests, regression tests, performance tests, and product documentation tests. For each type of test, test cases should be identified, along with detailed test steps and expected results. For this purpose, most organizations prepare formal test plans, and test cases (also called test specifications or test procedures). As previously stated, these documents should be reviewed with appropriate departments.

During test execution, test results should be recorded, and they should be compared against expected results to determine if the tests are successful. In case of test failure, identified defect(s) should be formally logged and resolved by following a defined defect management process. Detailed results of test execution, in the form of test logs, should be maintained. The results of testing, including defects reported, should be compiled in a formal test report.

When COTS or in-house test tools are to be acquired for use in the testing process, then acceptance criteria for the tools should be established, and suitability of the test tools should be assessed against the established criteria, prior to their use in the test process. This can be accomplished by formally identifying tool requirements. In the case of COTS tools, a comparative assessment of the candidate tools can then be performed to determine which tool best meets the identified requirements, while in the case of in-house tools, tool development should be in accordance with the stated tool requirements.

This subclause also requires that the records of validation and of actions taken be maintained. For this purpose, validation records, such as system test results and report(s), and review record(s) of product review against acceptance criteria must be controlled (in accordance with subclause 4.2.4). Again, evidence must be available to demonstrate that actions requested at such reviews, and defects found during system testing, were properly handled.

Finally, note that testing, especially system testing, though the most common means to perform validation, is not the only one. A product may be validated by additional means, as appropriate, such as acceptance testing, configuration audits, and inspections. Again, when such validation techniques are used, records of such validation, for example, acceptance test report(s), configuration audit report(s), and inspection records, must be maintained.

Subclause 7.3.7: Control of design and development changes

This subclause states that changes to design and development must be identified and appropriate records maintained. Further, in the event of a change, the proposed change must be reviewed for the impact of the change on current implementation and previous releases of the product, and the change must be verified and validated, as appropriate, before it is approved and incorporated in the product. It is mandatory that the records of such review of changes and consequent actions be maintained.

In the context of software development, control of changes to design and development falls in the realm of configuration control, which is a key function of configuration management. Because configuration control involves first identifying the configuration itself (configuration identification), and traceability of changes to it, explanation of this subclause is deferred to the related subclause 7.5.3.

CLAUSE 7.4: PURCHASING

Subclause 7.4.1: Purchasing process

Before we examine the requirements stated under this subclause, it is necessary to be familiar with what is meant by a *purchased product*. In the context of the software industry, purchased product includes, but is not limited to: third-party software, hardware, contract personnel, business process outsourcing, product documentation, and training material. Use of third-party software in the following situations can be regarded as equivalent to the use of a purchased product:

1. The organization produces a software product that *includes* third-party software—either COTS software (also called *bundled software*), or subcontracted software.

2. The organization uses third-party software *during* its internal product development process, for example, COTS or in-house developed software tools, such as defect (or change) management tools and software test tools.

3. The organization's product requires use of third-party software in *conjunction* with it, such as commercial database software.

ISO 90003 clarifies that for the purpose of this requirements subclause, even free software, that is, freeware and shareware, is regarded as purchased software.

To better understand the requirements that follow, let's consider the purchasing process in the software industry using an example of purchase of third-party software for inclusion in a product (hereafter referred to as software acquisition). Note that software acquisition may also be for purposes other than inclusion in the product. For example, there may be a need to procure third-party software as part of an organization's IT infrastructure requirements, for example, antivirus software or word processing software. An example of a software acquisition process is as follows.

A project is launched to develop a software product. During the design phase, the software engineers are confronted with a build versus buy decision for certain software components required in the product. A decision is made to buy the required software. The software development organization documents the requirements for the required software, and potential vendors are invited to demonstrate their products. Some vendors are short-listed after a preliminary review of their ability to meet the organization's requirements, as well as preliminary acceptance of the vendors' business terms.[12] Additionally, the best short-listed products are procured on an evaluation (or trial) license for an in-house pilot study. Based on the pilot results, the organization arrives at a purchase decision. This is then followed by contractual negotiations and finalization of the terms of the sale before placement of a purchase order.

Having discussed purchasing in the context of the software industry, we can now examine the requirements in this subclause. This subclause requires the organization to ensure that the purchased product meets the requirements specified for it.

In order to ensure compliance of the purchased product to stated requirements, the product must be verified against the requirements during the purchasing process. This entails verification of the product *before* a purchase decision is made (hereafter referred to as preliminary review), and also *after* the product has been purchased (hereafter referred to as verification of purchased product). Discussion on verification of purchased product is deferred to the explanation of the related subclause 7.4.3. In order to facilitate a preliminary review of the product, purchase requirements must be identified by the organization (as per subclause 7.4.2).

One possible way of assessing a product against requirements is as follows: products under consideration may be assigned a score for how best they comply with each requirement. For this purpose, a four-point scale can be utilized for awarding points based on whether the product is best-in-class (score = 3), meets the requirement (score = 2), partially meets the requirement (score = 1), or fails to meet the requirement (score = 0). Further, each requirement, depending on its relative importance, can be assigned a weight that can be multiplied by the requirement *score* to arrive at the *element score* for each product under consideration (refer to product assessment matrix in Table 7.1). In this example, the *maximum possible score* of 75 represents the best score an organization can achieve, that is, if it is assessed as best-in-class (score = 3) for each requirement; the *minimum required score* of 50 is based on minimally each requirement being met (score = 2). The *overall rating* is a score that indicates how best the product meets all the requirements. Note that it may not be possible to rate each product based solely on a product demonstration. However, based on the demonstration, minimally, it should be possible to determine compliance to key requirements, and it can then be decided whether it is desirable to perform a formal evaluation of the product. It may only be possible to complete the product assessment matrix upon completion of the formal product evaluation. In Table 7.1, assessment results show that product 1 is slightly superior to product 2. Product 3 fails to meet the minimum required score to stay in contention for selection. Therefore, at this point product 1 may be recommended for selection, or both products 1 and 2 may be evaluated further for comparison of financial and business terms of sale before a final decision is made.

The aforementioned approach can be adapted for assessing a potential supplier for outsourcing software development, although in this case, a formal quality evaluation of the potential vendor should also be performed. Many organizations that are registered to ISO 9000 require their suppliers to be ISO 9000 registered as well. This is because it provides the organization a high degree of assurance that its suppliers will operate in a similar fashion since they would be governed by the same quality standard. However, for various business reasons, it is not always possible to restrict

Table 7.1 Product assessment matrix to determine compliance to purchase requirements.

Requirements Category	ID	Requirement	Weight	Product 1		Product 2		Product 3	
				Score	Element Score	Score	Element Score	Score	Element Score
			1 Minor 2 Major 3 Critical	0 Fails reqrt. 1 Partially met 2 Meets reqrt. 3 Best-in-class	Weight × Score	0 Fails reqrt. 1 Partially met 2 Meets reqrt. 3 Best-in-class	Weight × Score	0 Fails reqrt. 1 Partially met 2 Meets reqrt. 3 Best-in-class	Weight × Score
Functional requirements	**FUN01**	\<Text of FUN01 requirement>	3	2	6	2	6	0	0
	FUN02	\<Text of FUN02 requirement>	2	3	6	2	4	0	0
	FUN03	\<Text of FUN03 requirement>	2	2	4	2	4	2	4
	FUN04	\<Text of FUN04 requirement>	1	1	1	3	3	1	1
	FUN05	\<Text of FUN05 requirement>	3	2	6	2	6	2	6
		Requirements Category Total			*23*		*23*		*11*
Performance requirements	**PER01**	\<Text of PER01 requirement>	3	3	9	2	6	1	3
	PER02	\<Text of PER02 requirement>	3	3	9	2	6	1	3
	PER03	\<Text of PER03 requirement>	2	2	4	2	4	2	4
		Requirements Category Total			*22*		*16*		*10*
Other requirements	**OTH01**	\<Text of OTH01 requirement>	3	2	6	2	6	1	3
	OTH02	\<Text of OTH02 requirement>	3	2	6	3	9	2	6
		Requirements Category Total			*12*		*15*		*9*
		Overall Rating *(Max. Possible Score: 75, Min. Required Score: 50)*			*57*		*54*		*30*

the supplier selection process to ISO 9000–registered suppliers only. That is, an ISO 9000–registered supplier may be preferable but is not always necessary. Neither does ISO 9000 require that for an organization to be ISO 9000 registered, its suppliers be ISO 9000 registered as well. Irrespective of whether or not a potential supplier is ISO 9000 registered, it is always preferable for an organization to independently determine the quality of its potential supplier by performing an evaluation itself. This is because due to the subjective nature of auditing, inconsistencies in audits conducted by different registrars, and due to the fact that ISO 9001:2000, by design, does not prescribe a particular way of complying with a requirement, there are bound to be differences in the *quality* of the QMS established by different ISO 9000–registered suppliers. In other words, though two ISO 9000–registered organizations may have sound QMSs in place, the QMS of one organization may be distinctly superior to the QMS of the other organization.

This subclause also states that the organization must evaluate and select suppliers based on their ability to meet the organization's requirements. Furthermore, it is required that criteria for supplier evaluation, selection, and reevaluation be established. Therefore, the organization must identify a list of criteria that are to be used in any supplier evaluation; a list of criteria that must be met for a supplier to be selected; and a list of criteria that may trigger a supplier reevaluation. For example, an organization may require that, to be considered for selection, the supplier must be ISO 9000 registered. Similarly, the organization may require all suppliers to be reevaluated annually. Insofar as assessing the ability of a potential supplier is concerned, a systematic approach should be followed for supplier evaluation and selection. As an example, let's consider a typical process for subcontractor evaluation and selection for subcontracted software development. This process usually begins with all potential subcontractors being supplied a preliminary quality questionnaire. The questionnaire probes whether the subcontractor has a formal QMS in place; requests a copy of the subcontractor's quality manual and key procedures; and generally probes for use of key quality practices in the organization, such as review and verification activities. The responses to this questionnaire can help in performing an initial filtering exercise to weed out unsuitable subcontractors. The second step of the process involves an on-site evaluation of the subcontractor by the organization's quality department. This is a critical step to distinguish between subcontractors, all of whom may have achieved the common benchmark of being ISO 9000 registered. For this purpose, Table 7.1 can be adapted to include quality requirements that the potential subcontractor is required to comply with. As an example, all or some key requirements from a quality standard such as ISO 9001:2000 can be used as the quality requirements for such an evaluation.

This subclause also states that records must be kept of the results of the evaluation and actions arising from the evaluation. Therefore, when such an on-site evaluation is performed, the results should be included in a formal evaluation report. When a particular subcontractor is selected, the organization should pursue corrective and/or preventive action with the subcontractor in the areas identified for improvement from the evaluation. The records of the evaluation and of any corrective and/or preventive actions arising from the evaluation must be maintained. Once a subcontractor has been selected, it should be added to the organization's official approved supplier list that lists all the approved suppliers of the organization along with their contact information. No material for use in product or service delivery should be procured from suppliers who are not included in the approved supplier list.

This subclause also states that once a supplier had been selected, the type and extent of control exercised over the supplier and product must be commensurate with the criticality of the purchased product in the organization's SPDP, as well as impact on the resulting product. For example, if an organization is purchasing COTS software for use in its SPDP (such as a CM tool) and *not* for inclusion in its product, then the assessment is most likely to be limited to the quality and capability of the software, and to the viability of the supplier. In such a situation, an assessment of the supplier's QMS is not generally performed. On the other hand, if an organization has subcontracted software development, then a greater degree of control over the subcontractor is required. This is because the subcontracted software will have a significant and direct impact on the quality of the end product. Typically in such a situation, the organization will specify quality-related requirements to be met by the supplier *during* the product development process (refer to related subclause 7.4.2), require periodic meetings and joint reviews with the supplier, and additionally communicate its intention to perform periodic surveillance quality audits of the supplier. The controls that an organization generally uses to monitor and control performance of its suppliers should be documented in its supplier management procedure(s). The controls to be applied to a specific supplier should be specified in the respective contractual agreement with the supplier, and in the organization's supplier management procedures. Subcontractor control activities should be addressed in the respective project plans, as appropriate.

Due to the unique nature of third-party software, there are some additional issues that should be addressed in the procurement and use of such software, such as:

- Identification of third-party software:

  – Are the versions and patch levels of all third-party software used in the product identifiable? It is necessary to obtain this information for various reasons. For example, if defects are found in the organization's product that are attributed to the bundled software, then the organization has to contact the third-party software supplier for reporting the defect against a specific version and patch level of the third-party software.

- Control of third-party software:

  – Have mechanisms been established for configuration management control of third-party software?

- Defect management for third-party software:

  – When newer patches for the third-party software become available, has the organization assigned responsibilities to someone to assess whether the new patches should be installed?

  – Has responsibility been assigned for the installation of approved patches? In other words, has the organization established mechanisms to preclude the unauthorized installation of patches? For example, are the employees allowed to arbitrarily procure the latest third-party software patches directly from the supplier and install them on their machines? This introduces the configuration management problem of potentially having different versions and patch levels of the same software installed (and in use) on different machines!

  – For defects found in bundled software, has the organization established a suitable time frame with its suppliers for the resolution of those defects? Is this time frame *within the bounds* of the time frame that the organization has contractually agreed to with its own customers for defects reported against the end product? For example, say the organization commits to its customers that it will fix all reported critical defects in its product within 48 hours. Now, in a case where a reported critical defect is attributed in whole or in part to the bundled software, the defect fix from the supplier should be received within an acceptable time frame. An acceptable time frame would be one that does not preclude the organization from meeting its own commitment to the end customer (that it will rectify any critical problem within 48 hours). Therefore, for this purpose, the organization may require its supplier to fix critical defects attributed to the bundled software within 24 hours.

• Discontinuance of third-party software: When the end-of-life of the third-party software is prior to the end-of-life of the organization's product in which it is bundled, does the organization provide a patch to its customers to upgrade them to a currently supported release of the third-party software?

The organization's QMS should also contain provisions to remove a supplier from the approved supplier list, if deemed necessary. This may be warranted in situations such as a supplier repeatedly ignoring quality recommendations from the organization, history of unsatisfactory supplier performance (as evidenced by poor supplier performance metrics and/or audit results), and history of ineffective corrective actions by the supplier in response to audit findings.

Subclause 7.4.2: Purchasing information

This subclause requires that purchasing information provided to a supplier accurately describe what is being purchased. If appropriate, purchasing information must include requirements for approval of the purchased product, and for approval of procedures, processes, and equipment used by the supplier. When appropriate, purchase requirements must include QMS requirements, and competence requirements for subcontract personnel.

To comply with this requirement, it must be ensured that purchasing information is clearly stated in the purchase order or contractual agreement, and formal requirements document, as appropriate. Such information includes but is not limited to:

• Information to uniquely identify the product ordered, such as product name, and product number and version.

• Specification of product requirements. For example, in case of subcontracted software, requirements should be communicated by means of a formal requirements document, similar to the PRD or SRS the organization uses for its internal product development. If the requirements are not completely known at the time of finalization of the purchase order or contract, then a reference should be provided to how the requirements will be determined and approved.

• Design and development constraints placed on the supplier, such as required use of a specific programming language.

- Information on intended use of the purchased product, what environment it will be used in, and, if applicable, interfaces of the purchased product with other entities in the end product.

- Acceptance criteria for the purchased product.

- Requirements pertaining to required competency of supplier personnel. For example, an organization may require that certain employees of its supplier be formally trained and/or professionally certified in a required skill.

- QMS requirements, such as requirement to collect and report measurement data for specific quality metrics requested by the organization; required use of specific processes mandated by the organization; required adherence to specific workmanship standards, such as a software coding standard provided by the organization; requirement to create specific records required by the organization; and so on.

This subclause also requires the organization to ensure that the purchase requirements are adequate before they are communicated to the supplier. In order to ensure this, the guidance provided under explanation of subclause 7.2.2 can be utilized. For example, purchase requirements should be reviewed with appropriate personnel within the organization, prior to communication to the supplier.

Subclause 7.4.3: Verification of purchased product

This subclause states that the organization must implement appropriate verification mechanisms to ensure that the purchased product meets the specified purchase requirements.

For the purpose of verification of purchased product, when appropriate, contractual negotiations should include agreement on acceptance criteria for the purchased product. This concept of establishment of acceptance criteria by the organization for a product purchased from its supplier is similar to the concept of establishment of acceptance criteria between the organization and its customers. For example, such an approach is typically adopted by an organization when it subcontracts software development to another company. Once the product is received, it should be verified against the acceptance criteria prior to formal acceptance by the organization. In the case of purchase of COTS software for inclusion in a product, such verification is typically performed prior to a purchase decision, and the final verification may be in the form of a quick check to ensure that the correct product and version has been received, followed by more exhaustive verification in the form of testing of the purchased product after integrating it with the organization's own product.

This subclause also states that if the organization, or its customer(s), intend to verify the product at the supplier's premises, then this must be stated in the purchasing information (such as purchase order, or contract). As stated in the explanation of subclause 7.2.3, if appropriate, the customer may participate in verification activities with the organization during product development. The analogous situation occurs when the organization engages a subcontractor for software development. In this case, the organization is a customer of its subcontractor. Therefore, it should participate, as appropriate, in verification activities with its subcontractor. It should also be verified that suitable means are available to uniquely identify the product in case anomalies are found and need to be corrected. Stating the verification arrangement in the purchasing information ensures that the arrangement is formally agreed to, and it also ensures that the supplier is contractually bound to involve the organization in the verification activities. Additionally, this subclause states that the relationship between such verification performed at the supplier's premises and authorization for release of the purchased product must be determined and stated in the purchasing information. For example, it may be agreed that release of the product by the supplier may not proceed until the organization has completed on-site verification, and/or otherwise provided its consent for release of the purchased product at a joint milestone review meeting held with the supplier.

If the organization uses the services of contract personnel, who in essence constitute a purchased product, then it should verify the competence of the contract personnel by examining their competency records, and address deficiencies in required competencies (refer to related guidance under explanation of subclause 6.2.2).

If the purchased product is data, then it should be verified that the data's content and accuracy meets the organization's needs and it is provided in a form, medium, and volume that is acceptable to the organization.

CLAUSE 7.5: PRODUCTION AND SERVICE PROVISION

Subclause 7.5.1: Control of production and service provision

This subclause requires that software production and service provision be planned and executed under controlled conditions. Controlled conditions include but are not limited to: information on characteristics of the product, availability of work instructions for use during the process, availability and use of suitable equipment to execute the activities, availability and use of suitable devices to monitor and measure the executed activities, and implementation of activities for release, delivery, and post-delivery.

In the context of the software industry, control of production and service provision covers:

- *Release activities.* These entail developing the software (including creation of software builds of the integrated software components), preparing the release package, and replicating the master copy of the software for delivery to the customer.

- *Delivery and installation activities.* These include activities pertaining to delivery and installation of the product.

- *Maintenance and technical support activities.* These include activities performed after product release to rectify defects reported against the product, manage requests for changes to the product, and cover all aspects of technical support.

In order to comply with this requirements subclause, it is best to examine its implications on the execution of each of the aforementioned activities, as described next.

Release activities. To facilitate consistency during software production, the organization should establish a set of programming rules and naming conventions that should be documented in a software coding standard. It should be recognized that the software product, once released, will have to be maintained by personnel who are typically not the original developers of the product. Therefore, it is very important that the entire software product exhibit consistency in the application of programming rules and naming conventions. Adherence to the software coding standard should be monitored during code reviews. Appropriate tools should be used in software development, such as automated tools that enforce adherence to the organization's software coding standard, tools to detect memory leaks, and so on.

The organization should define a release hierarchy for its products, and the quality of releases within the release hierarchy (such as alpha, beta, or GA quality). For example, a software product organization may establish its product hierarchy as follows:

1. *Product generation.* A product generation represents major functional enhancements to the product, and possibly new or revised architecture. Software defect fixes are also included in a new product generation.

2. *Major release (or service pack).* A major release represents new functional enhancements within a product generation. Software defect fixes are also included in a new major release.

3. *Minor release.* A minor release implies that a number of software defects have been included in the release and no new functionality is included.

4. *Software patch.* A software patch represents an emergency fix to a software defect.

Of these, only software patches are sent on an as-needed basis, while the other releases are generally scheduled in advance.

For each of these, the organization should identify what software items constitute the software release, and how and where defect fixes are to be applied. For example, in the case of a new product generation or major release, all required functionality as specified in the PRD, must be included. In the case of minor releases, the included defect fixes are typically applied on top of the latest major release (within the latest product generation), and automatically *propagated forward* to future releases as software development progresses from this latest baseline of the source code. However, depending on the criticality of the defect and customer need, if necessary, the fix may *also* have to be applied on an earlier release that is still in use. In other words, the fix may have to be *propagated backward*. Similarly, if the defect originated in an old product generation, and it has to be fixed on the same product generation due to customer need, then, if the defect persists on subsequent product generations, the fix needs to be *propagated forward* to the appropriate releases. The instructions for generating the software build of the different types of releases should be consistent with what is required to be included in a particular type of release. For example, software patches do not require the complete software product to be rebuilt and rereleased.

If an organization delivers its software product on physical media, such as a CD, by replicating a copy for release from the master copy, then the following considerations should be addressed:

• The media on which the product is delivered should be in accordance with the delivery media specified in the contract.

• The master copy and the replicated copy should have unique configuration identification labels that help identify the variant and version of the software product. A product may be offered in various variants depending on customer need, where each variant represents a different configuration of the product—with certain features disabled or not included, or optional components enabled or included. The configuration identification label should provide pertinent information, such as an indication of whether the subject item is the master copy, or a copy of the master. In the latter case, it should be possible to deduce the identity of the master from the configuration identification of its copy. Further explanation on configuration identification is included under explanation of subclause 7.5.3.

• It should be ensured that required product documentation is provided with the replicated copy. Again, this generally requires that the configuration item numbering convention be established such that it is possible to deduce from the configuration identification of the product documentation which specific version of the product it is associated with. A sample configuration item numbering convention is included in explanation of subclause 7.5.3.

• It should be ensured that only authorized personnel have access to master copies of the software product, and to the equipment used to create replicated copies. If certain replicated copies are prepared in advance, they, along with the master copy, should be stored in a secure location. The replication equipment should also be protected from software viruses to preclude contamination of the delivered product.

• Once a replicated copy has been produced, a verification mechanism should be in place to ensure that it indeed is a true copy. This can be performed using automated compare tools, and by performing a minimum functional test (sanity test) using the replicated copy.

Delivery and Installation Activities. The product should be delivered in accordance with the arrangements stipulated in the contract. The product release package should be verified by using a release checklist to ensure that the package contents are complete. Guidance on preservation of the product during delivery is deferred to explanation of related subclause 7.5.5.

Installation of the product is generally performed by the customer, in which case the organization should provide the customer with installation instructions in the product documentation. The installation instructions should list the required resources, information, and documentation required for the installation, along with description of expected results at each step. Just as any other product documentation, the installation instructions should be reviewed and additionally tested prior to delivery to the customer. Bear in mind that an erroneous installation instruction leaves a poor first impression on the customer.

In certain situations, the organization may install the software product for the customer. In such situations, the organization should ensure that it has addressed items such as:

• Agreement on an installation schedule with the customer. This may be especially important if the installation will be rolled out at multiple customer sites.

- Arrangements for access to the customer site(s).

- Agreement on roles and responsibilities of the organization and the customer regarding installation activity. For example, the organization may be required to provide informal training to the customer's employees on the installation process.

- Clarification on the need for installation instructions, if appropriate.

- Clarification on preinstallation tasks, for example, the organization may require the customer to perform certain hardware configuration tasks prior to software installation.

- Agreement on the acceptance criteria for the installation.

- Provision of competent personnel for installing the product at the customer site(s).

Maintenance and Technical Support Activities. The organization should plan for and provide support to customers such that it adequately meets their needs. To this end, the organization should ensure that it provides customers with help-desk contact information for reporting of product defects during regular business hours, and, if appropriate, during off hours for critical failures. The technical support personnel must be competent and adequately trained. For example, they should be provided training on the organization's product and in troubleshooting skills. Further, the technical support personnel must be provided appropriate tools to enable them to execute their tasks effectively (as per clause 6.3). The organization should ensure that it has the capability to offer support to the customer in the event of a critical failure of its software at the customer site. This includes obtaining critical system information for debugging purposes (such as log files), and ability to provide on-site support, if contractually agreed. Further, the organization should ensure that its technical support tools are controlled in accordance with clause 6.3 requirements.

Generally, software development companies offer different levels of maintenance support to their customers, such as silver, gold, and platinum. The benefits increase with a higher-cost maintenance, and so do the demands on the organization delivering the services. Typically, maintenance support ceases upon the official end-of-life of the product, although organizations may charge additional fees for extended support beyond the standard support period. The product maintenance process of the organization should be defined, beginning with the receipt of a request for product maintenance, and ending with the closure of the maintenance request (refer to earlier discussion on customer calls management in chapter 3). In the case of software defect fixes, it should be validated that the defect has been resolved by replicating[13] the initially reported defect, and verifying that it does not recur. In the case of a product change request, the implemented functionality should be validated against the product change request to verify that it has been met.

The type and duration of maintenance support an organization has committed to a customer should be included in the respective contractual agreement. Additional items that should be considered for inclusion in the maintenance agreement include but are not limited to:

- *Method of requesting maintenance support.* For example, specification of how the organization may be contacted for maintenance support.

- *Scope of maintenance support.* Specification of what kind of requests constitute a valid request for maintenance. For example, maintenance is generally limited to product defects only, while a product change request entails additional cost for the customer in order to be implemented.

- *Definition of key terms.* Description of key terms, such as defect, defect severities, defect workaround, response time, and so on.

- *Specification of response time.* Specification of response times for the various defect severities, and agreement on financial penalty amounts if the response times are violated (if appropriate). On-site troubleshooting and maintenance activities generally entail additional cost for the customer.

- *Scheduled maintenance, if any.* For example, some organizations deliver minor releases with defect fixes at scheduled intervals.

- *Acceptance criteria for maintenance activity.* A maintenance request should generally not be closed until the customer who submitted the request concurs that the request has been fulfilled.

Maintenance records should be analyzed to identify opportunities for improvement to the product and the QMS. For example, a Pareto analysis of the customer-reported product defects could help identify software components with the greatest number of defects and this information can be used for directing improvements in those areas. Similarly, time-stamp data in the defect management tool can be analyzed to ascertain if the organization is complying with the response times agreed to with the customer, and for focusing improvement efforts in areas of greatest delay.

Finally, the organization should consider maintenance activities for internal tools as well, including fixing of identified defects and need for tool enhancements. For this purpose, the organization may utilize the product change request and defect management processes discussed previously.

Subclause 7.5.2: Validation of processes for production and service provision

This subclause requires that the processes for production and service provision be validated if the final output cannot be verified by monitoring or measurement. Validation of the processes provides the assurance that the process is capable of yielding desired results.

In order to comply with this requirement, the organization must examine if there are any organizational processes the output of which cannot be verified until after delivery to the customer. If so, alternate means must be used to provide the confidence that those processes are capable of delivering expected results. For example, if certain features of a product cannot be tested because the organization lacks the required test environment, then plans should be devised to compensate for the inability to validate the subject requirements, and mitigation of the associated risks. Refer to previous discussion on this specific example under explanation of subclause 7.3.6. Similarly, if the organization is planning a change to a process, all proposed changes to the process should be reviewed with appropriate parties to validate that the revised process will adequately meet all success criteria associated with the process. As an example, a failure mode and effects analysis (FMEA) may be performed to identify potential deficiencies in a process before it is approved, and to facilitate appropriate action to eliminate or reduce failure modes in the process.[14] In this case, once the identified deficiencies in the process have been eliminated, then the process must be revalidated before its approval.

Subclause 7.5.3: Identification and traceability

This subclause requires that the product be appropriately identified throughout the product development process. This subclause also requires that the status of the product with regard to planned monitoring and measurement activities be maintained.

In the context of the software industry, identification of the product and associated project documentation is accomplished by means of configuration management (CM). An overview of CM and its key functions was provided in chapter 3. The CM activities an organization establishes should be commensurate with its product size, complexity of the product, and associated risks. Following is a list of items that should be considered in defining the organization's CM process:

• *Planned activities.* CM activities should be specified for each of the key functions—configuration identification, configuration control, configuration status accounting, and configuration audits.

• *Roles and responsibilities.* Typically, organizations have a CM department that has the primary responsibility for facilitating the implementation of CM in the organization. However, effective implementation of CM practices cannot be achieved without the true commitment and active participation of other departments in the organization as well, especially the software development department. Therefore, the roles and responsibilities of various departments with regard to CM activities should be clearly identified.

• *Required CM tools.* CM tools should be selected and procured in accordance with guidance provided under explanation of clause 7.4.

• *Unique identification of name and version of each configuration item.* The numbering convention that is applied to all configuration items, including documents, must provide a unique identification for each distinct configuration item. An example of a document numbering convention was provided in chapter 3. Using that specific example, it is preferable to extend that numbering convention, such that it can be applied to all configuration items, including software products. An example of such a configuration item numbering convention is shown in Table 7.2.a.

• *Identification of when an item is to be placed under CM control.* Once an item is placed under formal CM control, then subsequent changes to it have to be executed and managed as per established CM processes. This entails a cost overhead due to the additional activities. Therefore, it should be carefully determined when the appropriate time is to place an item under formal CM control. As a general guideline, changes to an approved software baseline, or document, must be CM controlled. An item must be under CM control no later than the time of its initial approval, or sooner if the item will be used or referenced by personnel other than the item's producers. Also, any software tools in use (either in-house or third-party) should be placed under CM control.

• *Identification of the exact versions of constituent parts and accompanying documentation for a product.* The final version of the software product will comprise various items, such as software components (including third-party software), and associated project and product documentation. Each of these items may have different version levels associated with them because the number of changes that each item undergoes in arriving at its final approved state will vary. Knowing the exact versions of all the items that are associated with the released product is critically important for distribution to customers, and for managing future changes. Software

Table 7.2.a Example of a configuration item numbering convention.

Configuration Item Number Format: AA-BBB-CCC-DDDDDD-XXXX-YY

where,	
AA:	Two-character alpha identifier for organizational business unit or location.
	Note: "EX" denotes a configuration item of external origin, that is, from outside the organization.
BBB:	Three-character alpha identifier for the department that owns the configuration item.
	For example, SWE may represent software engineering
CCC:	Three-character alpha identifier that identifies the type of configuration item.
	For example, PRD may represent product requirements document; SCO may represent source code.
DDDDDD:	Six-character alphanumeric identifier to identify the product or project with which the configuration item is associated.
XXXX:	Four-character sequential number between 0001 and 9999. This sequential number uniquely identifies a specific configuration item (in the case of software product, it corresponds to the software build identifier to uniquely identify a specific variant and version of the software product).
YY:	Two-character alphanumeric identifier used as follows:
	When CCC is "SCO," YY may either be "MC" to indicate a master copy, or a two-digit number to uniquely identify the replicated copy.

Table 7.4.b Sample configuration item number (based on numbering convention in Table 7.2.a).

AA	BBB	CCC	DDDDDD	XXXX	YY	Explanation
DA	SWE	SCO	PRB42	0045	01	DA-SWE-SCO-PRB42-0045-01 is the source code **(SCO)** created by the software engineering department **(SWE)** at the Dallas **(DA)** location of the organization. The SCO is for the Probe product version 4.2 **(PRB42)** and it is the 45th **(0045)** software build (representing a unique variant and version of the software product). It is the first **(01)** replicated copy.

source-control and documentation management tools help manage such version information for each of the constituent items of a product. Additionally, the configuration item numbering convention may provide information on the relationship of a particular configuration item to a specific product.

• *Build status of products.* A software product may be built on different operating systems and platforms, using different environment parameters, and different build utilities or scripts. Such details, along with information on included software components, included defect fixes, relevant known issues (unresolved defects), build retrieval and installation instructions, and results of sanity tests of the build, should be documented in a build record. It should be possible to replicate a specific software build by using the information contained in its build record. Because the build record is typically used by other departments such as the system test department to assess whether the build is acceptable for use and to determine its contents, it should be distributed to relevant departments.

• *Control of concurrent updates to software items.* Source-control tools possess the capability to allow for source code to be checked out for updates by one software engineer, and another software engineer may only update the code once it has been checked in. Such tools also possess the capability to allow for simultaneous updates by engineers working independently, and a subsequent merge of the update code.

• *Control of multiple products in more than one location.* A product evolves through various generations, major and minor releases, and software patches. A customer, or different customers, may have different versions of the product installed at different locations, or at the same location. CM practices should be capable of supporting such different active baselines of the product, and incorporating defect fixes into them when required. Such support should continue until the end-of-life of a particular baseline, and expiry of all associated extended support agreements with customers. It is in the interest of the organization to prevent a proliferation of too many active baselines, and encourage customers to migrate to the latest software baseline.

• *Identification, tracking, and reporting of all actions and changes as a result of a change request or reported defect.* From the time a request to fix a product defect or change current functionality is submitted, the request and all associated actions and changes need to be tracked until closure. Defect or change management tools provide this capability by allowing for the capture of the:

  – *Request details.* This typically includes information such as identification of requestor, submission date, affected product, product component, severity of the request, problem or change description, reason for change, and replication steps (if applicable).

– *Analysis of the request.* This typically includes information such as identification of who analyzed the request, recommendation of the analyst (including confirmation of request severity), affected component or documentation, impact of change on other components (that is, regression test considerations), and anticipated effort.

– *CCB review of the proposed changes.* This includes information such as CCB review of the analysis; decision on approval, further analysis, or rejection[15]; identification of related action items (if any); and software release(s) in which the change will be delivered (if the request is approved).

– *Implementation and verification of the change.* This typically includes information such as identification of software module(s) updated, description of actual change, identification of the implementer, and results of review and verification of the change (for example, code review and unit test).

– *Validation of the change.* This typically includes identification of the system tester and results of validation of the change (that is, system test and regression test outcome).

It is recognized that it is generally inappropriate and onerous to handle all requests for change during design and development in accordance with the aforementioned formal process, for example, need to change an approved test specification, need for minor corrections to product documentation, and other such cases. However, in all cases, a proposed change must be reviewed with appropriate personnel, and the impact of implementing the change must be determined in advance (as per subclause 7.3.7). For example, a change to a parent document may cause its child document to be revised to maintain consistency.

• *Information on monitoring and measurement status of the product.*[16] In addition to tracking of review, verification, and validation of changes, CM practices should address review, verification, validation, and measurement status of new software development and associated documentation. For example, CM practices may mandate that, prior to inclusion in a formal software build, all software code must have been unit tested and code reviewed.

• *Release management and delivery.* CM practices should support the release and delivery activities as described under explanation of subclause 7.5.1.

The CM plan for a project should describe how the activities of the CM process will be executed in the specific project. Therefore, it should contain project-specific information, such as schedule for CM activities, identification of CM personnel assigned to the project, specification of the configuration identification for the project artifacts, and deviations, if any, from the CM process (as an example, refer to *IEEE Std 828-1998*). Because various departments have the responsibility to assist the CM department in the execution of CM activities, the project CM plan should be reviewed and approved with participants from appropriate departments.

Finally, this subclause states that when traceability of an artifact is required, such as traceability of the code for a software component to the applicable design, and traceability of a documented design to applicable requirements, then the subject artifact and the element traced to—both must be uniquely identifiable.

This requirement can be met by including a forward traceability matrix in the parent document, and a backward traceability matrix in the child document. Generally, forward traceability is used to provide the assurance that each parent requirement *will be* addressed in the design, implementation, and test. Backward traceability is used to provide the assurance that each item in the child document *has addressed* what is explicitly or implicitly required by its parent document. Therefore, completed traceability matrices serve as a valuable mechanism to monitor that requirements are designed in, implemented, and tested in the product. For example, a requirements traceability matrix should trace applicable PRD requirements to the appropriate SRS. Note that if there are certain requirements in the PRD that are allocated to hardware, then they need to be traced forward to the appropriate hardware requirements specification (HRS). A complete PRD to SRS (and HRS, if applicable) traceability matrix thus shows how all the system requirements have been allocated to hardware and software subsystems. The requirements for the interfaces between software subsystems, software and hardware, and the resulting product and external systems should be specified in the appropriate requirements documents, and either designed in the appropriate software and hardware design documents, or in stand-alone interface design documents. Each SRS and HRS requirement should be traced to the applicable PRD requirements. A traceability matrix should trace each SRS requirement to the appropriate software or hardware design document, and further, each design element in the design documents should trace to the applicable SRS/HRS requirements[17]; each software module should trace to the applicable SDD section by using appropriate prologues in the software code. System test plans should trace each PRD and SRS requirement to individual system test cases. An example of one such traceability table for a "Software Product 'A,' Version 2.0," which has two SRSs—S1 and S2, is shown in Table 7.3.

In addition to the aforementioned documentation traceability, traceability information should be available for all defect fixes and product

Table 7.3 System test case traceability matrix.

PRD Requirement	SRS Requirement	System Test Case ID
A20_FUNC1	A20_S1_FUNC1	A20_TST1
	A20_S1_FUNC2	A20_TST2
A20_FUNC2	A20_S2_FUNC1	A20_TST3
A20_FUNC3	A20_S1_FUNC3	A20_TST4
A20_DIAG1	A20_S2_DIAG1	A20_TST5
A20_PERF1	A20_S2_PERF1	A20_TST6

changes delivered in a specific release. Again, defect and change management tools provide this information by supporting querying for all defect fixes and change requests associated with a specific software release. If appropriate, the customer service organization should also maintain a traceability table to trace which specific variant and version of the product is in use by a specific customer, or at a specific customer site. The organization should identify need for traceability in other processes based on organizational need or contractual obligation to customers.

Subclause 7.5.4: Customer property

This subclause states that if the organization uses customer-supplied property, then it must identify all such customer-supplied property, verify it for correctness, protect it, and address maintenance of the customer-supplied property.

In this requirement, customer-supplied property may refer to any of the following items supplied by the customer: a product that is to be incorporated in the organization's product; a product that is to be used by the organization during the SPDP; test data or operational use data; computer hardware equipment; specifications; development environment; and intellectual property. In order to identify customer-supplied property, when appropriate, the configuration item numbering convention can be used to convey that the item is of external origin (refer to Table 7.2.a). If the customer-supplied property is computer hardware equipment, it should be tagged with the assigned configuration item number. If such computer hardware equipment is required to be eventually returned to the customer, a log should be maintained to keep a record of the requested return dates for all equipment.

When a customer-supplied property is received, it must be verified by the organization to ensure it is acceptable and useful for the purpose for which it was acquired. For this purpose, during contractual negotiations or requirements discussions with the customer, it should be ensured that needed customer-supplied equipment is clearly identified, along with any associated requirements, as appropriate. Then, when the property is received, it must be verified against the specified requirements. This may be done by following the guidance provided under explanation of subclause 7.4.3.

The contractual agreement should also address who is responsible for maintenance of such property—a responsibility that typically belongs to the customer. However, this task may be performed by the organization if the associated costs are agreed with the customer. When the customer provides software that is to be incorporated into the organization's product, then issues pertaining to third-party software that were previously discussed under explanation of subclause 7.4.1 come into play and should be addressed. The organization must ensure that the customer property is secured from unauthorized access and tampering, and it is protected from disasters or loss, for example, by being backed up on-site (in case of software items), and by storing a backup copy at an escrow location.

Finally, this subclause requires that when any customer property is lost, damaged, or deemed unfit for use, then the customer must be notified and records maintained. Customer communication records in the form of e-mail records or copies of written communication are acceptable. The replacement of the subject property should be in accordance with what was contractually agreed to handle such situations.

Subclause 7.5.5: Preservation of product

This subclause requires that the organization preserve the product, and its constituent parts, both during internal processing, as well as during delivery to the customer. This covers identification, handling, packaging, storage, and protection of the product.

To comply with this requirement, the organization must ensure that from the time of production of a specific product version, until its delivery to the customer, the product is preserved and protected from being inadvertently altered, accidentally destroyed, or compromised. Due to its very nature, software does not degrade. However, there is the risk that the replicated copy may not be a true copy of the master (due to errors during replication), or viruses may accidentally get inserted in the product, or the delivery media may be damaged during handling and physical transportation, and so on.

In order to preclude the aforementioned situations, some of the precautions that should be considered include but are not limited to:

- CM control of each software release version, including ability to recreate a specific version from build records

- Periodic full and incremental backups of the software code and data, and storage in an escrow location for recovery in disaster situations

- Preventing unauthorized access to master and replicated copies of the product

- Use of software utilities to compare the replicated copy with its master

- Use of antivirus software to continuously scan the computer hardware equipment and delivery media

- Use of antistatic protection for items susceptible to electrostatic discharge (ESD) damage

- Appropriate packaging of the product, such as jewel cases for CDs

It is recommended that, prior to delivery, a packaging and labeling audit be performed to verify that the product package is correct, complete, and labeled in accordance with the organization's established requirements.

CLAUSE 7.6: CONTROL OF MONITORING AND MEASURING DEVICES

This clause requires the organization to identify monitoring and measurement activities to verify conformance of the product to requirements. Processes for monitoring and measurement must be established such that they are adequate to meet monitoring and measurement requirements.

Means for monitoring and measurement of a software product include reviews, verification activities, validation activities, and use of product metrics. Therefore, in essence, these requirements can be met by following the guidance provided for the related subclauses 7.3.4, 7.3.5, 7.3.6, and 8.2.4.

The crux of this requirements clause is a set of requirements pertaining to the identification and calibration of monitoring and measuring devices. In the context of the software development industry, monitoring and measuring devices include computer hardware equipment, software tools (developed in-house, COTS, or customer-supplied), test data, and ancillary equipment required to interface with computer hardware. In the explanation of clauses 4.1 and 6.1, it was stated that the need for required resources, which includes the need for monitoring and measuring devices, should be identified in the respective QMS procedures. These should be further specified and planned for use in a specific project by being identified in the respective project plans.

This clause also requires that, when necessary to ensure accuracy of results, measuring devices must be calibrated or verified prior to first use, or periodically, to provide assurance of their integrity for performing measurements. Such calibration or verification must be performed against industry-accepted measurement standards; when no such measurement standards exist, which is typical of the software development industry, the basis for calibration or verification must be recorded. The calibration or verification status of measuring devices must be known and periodically monitored for timely corrective action. Measuring devices must be secured from damage, deterioration, and tampering (or corruption).

Traditionally, calibration has been viewed as a concept alien to software development. It has been viewed as being more relevant to the manufacturing industry for calibration of devices such as screw gauges and vernier calipers. However, monitoring and measuring devices exist in the context of the software development industry as well. Therefore, let's examine these requirements within the context of the software development industry:

As stated previously under explanation of subclauses 7.4.3 and 7.5.4, purchased product and customer-supplied property need to be verified at the time of acquisition. This clause further extends this requirement for measuring devices, by stating that, additionally, calibration and verification be performed *periodically*. In the software development industry, such verification of software tools may need to be performed periodically or continuously, depending on the situation. For example, software tools and computer hardware need to be continuously monitored for introduction of viruses. However, a software test tool only needs to be reverified at the time of an update to the tool, say at the time of installation of a new software patch provided by the tool vendor. For example, say an organization has purchased a COTS software test tool. Before using the tool in a future project, a determination should be made of what latest release and software patches are available for the tool. If the organization currently uses an older version of the tool, then it should verify the newer version of the tool prior to deploying it. Say the organization currently uses version 1.0 of a COTS software test tool. Now, if the vendor releases a new version 2.0 of the tool, then, prior to deploying the tool, the organization should execute a subset of its existing baselined test cases and scripts using the updated tool to ascertain if the test results are the same as those obtained with the version of the tool it currently uses. The organization may realize that it incorrectly installed or configured the new version of the tool, or worse, use of the new version of the tool may require the old test scripts to be modified. Appropriate action should then be taken to ensure that the updated tool provides test results consistent with those provided by the earlier version of the tool. One can observe that the described scenario is akin to the concept of calibration of manufacturing test equipment to ensure *continued validity* of results.

Let us consider another example, where the software test tool is an in-house developed tool. In this case, prior to the tool's initial release, it should be verified that the tool meets all the requirements specified for the test tool. Also, part of the verification of any future revisions of the tool, it should be verified that the test tool's results are consistent with those obtained with the prior version of the tool. Discrepancies, if any, should be resolved prior to releasing the tool for use. If a monitoring or measuring device is used and subsequently found to be defective (or uncalibrated), then corrective action must be undertaken to rectify it and reassess the product on which it was used. For example, the product may need to be retested with the corrected device. Note that ISO 90003 recommends that the organization document a procedure describing how the test software is verified prior to use.

In order to secure the monitoring and measuring devices from unauthorized access, and to protect them from damage or loss, they should be placed under CM control, and they should be preserved as per guidance provided under explanation of subclause 7.5.5.

Finally, this clause requires that calibration and verification records be maintained. For example, the organization should maintain records to demonstrate that software test tools developed in house were verified prior to use. Records of the calibration standard used, if no international or national standard is used, must also be maintained. For example, for the software test tool examples described in this section, the organization should maintain (under CM control) the subset of baselined test cases and scripts that are executed to verify each new version of the software test tool. Records of validity of measurements taken with defective or uncalibrated equipment must also be maintained. For example, if it were subsequently discovered that the software test tool used during system testing had a defect, then those test cases that were not impacted by the noted defect need not be executed again. This may occur if the defect only impacts a specific usage scenario for the tool. In this case, the rationale for not re-executing the already executed test cases may be documented in the system test report.

ENDNOTES

1. Here, a project may also refer to a product or contract.
2. As an example, refer to *IEEE 730-2002: IEEE Standard for Software Quality Assurance Plans*, or *ISO 10005:1995 Quality Management—Guidelines for Quality Plans*.
3. Approval of the listed deviations is implicit once the project quality plan is formally approved. Also, if preferable, instead of listing the deviations in this project quality plan, they may be listed in the respective project plans. For

example, deviations from the standard system test process may be identified in the system test plan.

4. Boehm, B., *Software Engineering Economics* (Englewood Cliffs, NJ: Prentice Hall, 1982).

5. Conte, S. D. et al., *Software Engineering Metrics and Models* (Boston: Benjamin Cummings, 1986).

6. A review may be a formal review (inspection), or an informal review.

7. Fagan, M., "Advances in Software Inspections," *IEEE Transactions on Software Engineering* 12, no. 7 (1986).

8. This is typically accomplished by providing a document called product release notes.

9. Redundancy between the project plan and other planning documents, such as the project quality plan, should be avoided. Therefore, information already provided in the project quality plan should be omitted from the project plan.

10. See note 4.

11. This is specifically required by clause 8.3. Because validation is "verification against product requirements," therefore, the requirements pertaining to "reverification" in clause 8.3 are applicable here.

12. For example, a functionally superior product may have to be eliminated from contention if it is prohibitively expensive.

13. In certain situations, where the defect is unique to a customer's environment and can't be replicated by the organization, the organization should obtain necessary information from the customer to help debug the reported defect, and request validation of the fix by the customer before the reported defect is closed.

14. Johnson, K., "It's Fun to Work with F-M-E-A." *Quality Progress* (January 2002).

15. The CCB should use predefined criteria to determine when a request may be rejected. If a reported product defect or request for change is proposed to be rejected, the reason for request rejection should be reviewed in advance with the request submitter. This is especially important if the request was submitted by a customer. Further discussions with the request submitter may cause the CCB to revise its earlier decision.

16. ISO 90003 clarifies in explanation of subclause 8.2.4 that means for monitoring and measurement of a software product include reviews, verification, and validation. Note that measurements also entail the use of software product metrics that are discussed in explanation of subclause 8.2.4.

17. Note that, in the case of multiple SDDs, a full traceability table should be maintained that traces each SRS requirement to the applicable SDD. Additionally, if multiple SRSs exist, then there should be a separate traceability table for each SRS to underlying design documents. Alternatively, there may be one product traceability table that traces each PRD requirement to underlying SRSs and SDDs. This may also be implemented using an automated requirements management tool.

8

Measurement, Analysis, and Improvement Requirements

This chapter describes the requirements contained in the final requirements clause of ISO 9001:2000—clause 8. For the purpose of continuous improvement of an organization, this is the most important requirements clause in the standard because it contains requirements pertaining to monitoring and measuring the organization's product and processes, and continually improving them. This is accomplished by means such as customer satisfaction surveys, internal audits, metrics, and corrective and preventive actions.

CLAUSE 8.1: GENERAL

This clause states that the organization must plan and implement the monitoring, measurement (including statistical methods), analysis, and improvement processes used to:

- Demonstrate that the developed product conforms to product requirements.

- Ensure conformance to the QMS.

- Continually improve the QMS.

These general requirements pertaining to the product and the SPDP are further elaborated in clauses 8.2 to 8.5.

From a product perspective, monitoring and measurement processes are required to demonstrate that the product conforms to requirements. This requirement can be met by planning and implementing processes for product review, verification, validation, and measurement activities as per the general guidance in clause 4.1, and specific guidance in subclauses 7.3.4, 7.3.5, 7.3.6, and 8.2.4. Processes must also be planned and implemented for the analysis of *product measurements* to assess conformance of the product to requirements, and to identify opportunities for improvement and facilitate timely corrective and preventive action. This should be done by following the general guidance in clause 4.1, and specific guidance in clauses 8.4 and 8.5.

From a product realization perspective, monitoring and measurement processes are required to verify adherence to the QMS; to measure ability of the processes to meet planned objectives; and to assess customers' satisfaction with the organization's product and service quality, which in turn is a measure of the adequacy and effectiveness of the organization's QMS. This requirement can be met by planning and implementing the processes required for the underlying subclauses 8.2.1, 8.2.2, and 8.2.3; and by following the general guidance in clause 4.1 when defining these processes. Processes must also be planned and implemented for the analysis of *process measurements* to identify opportunities for process improvement, and to take timely corrective and preventive action. Again, this should be done by following the general guidance in clause 4.1, and specific guidance in clauses 8.4 and 8.5.

CLAUSE 8.2: MONITORING AND MEASUREMENT

Subclause 8.2.1: Customer satisfaction

This subclause requires the organization to measure customer satisfaction with regard to customers' requirements being met. The organization must also determine how customer satisfaction information will be collected and utilized.

This subclause is based on the premise that if an organization's QMS is adequate and effective, it should result in satisfied customers. However, if an organization's customers are dissatisfied, it provides a good reason to examine the organization's QMS for adequacy and effectiveness—although it is recognized that customer dissatisfaction may result from reasons beyond the scope of ISO 9001:2000. For example, customer dissatisfaction may result from reasons such as unrealistic expectations established by sales personnel prior to contractual negotiations for a new product, or the technical direction and future evolution of an organization's product being incompatible with a specific customer's needs. It is also generally recognized that measuring customer satisfaction makes good business sense because it is cheaper to retain current customers than attract new ones, and loyal customers offer high long-term returns to their suppliers and help attract new customers for their suppliers.

In order to comply with the requirements in this subclause, an organization should define and establish a customer satisfaction measurement process.[1] The scope of this process should cover the following major phases:

1. Planning

2. Execution

3. Analysis and corrective action planning

4. Results reporting and corrective action implementation

5. Follow-up

Each of these phases is briefly discussed next:

1. *Planning.* This phase entails preparing the customer satisfaction survey questionnaire and planning on how to administer the survey to customers. In preparing the questions for the survey, the organization should consider what issues are important from a customer perspective and devise questions accordingly. The survey should also contain questions to elicit customer feedback on areas that are regarded by the organization as possible areas of weakness, and that are directly or indirectly discernible from customer satisfaction data. For example, if the organization is concerned about the intuitiveness and usability of its product's graphical user interface, then appropriate questions should be devised to elicit customer feedback. The organization should also include questions that help it validate the acceptability of results of its quality metrics, and help in establishing target values (refer to discussion on measurements infrastructure under explanation of subclause 8.2.3). For example, if the organization uses metrics to measure responsiveness to the customer, then it can use the customer satisfaction survey to investigate whether the current level of responsiveness is acceptable to the customer, and to identify how much improvement is needed. Preferably, the survey should also elicit customer recommendations for organizational improvement in free text format.

The survey should be constructed so that the questions are categorized in logical groups, such as product quality, quality of customer service, and so on. There should be an appropriate response scale for each question. During this phase, decisions should also be made regarding how to administer the survey (by mail, or phone, or the Internet), who will administer the survey, how many and which customers to contact, who to contact at the customer locations, and other such administrative items. Finally, the survey should be pretested to gauge respondents' reactions to the survey layout and content. It should be administered to a few employees not involved in the development of the survey, or it may also be pretested with a small set of customers, if required. Upon completion of the pretest phase, revisions should be made to the survey, as needed.

2. *Execution.* During this phase the customer satisfaction survey is administered (as per the identified means) to the selected customers. When the customers are required to provide their responses by mail or the Internet, a reasonable time frame for accepting the responses should be established.

The results of the customer satisfaction survey should be compiled in a formal report with an executive summary. The report should provide a summary of overall customer satisfaction survey rating; customer satisfaction rating by customer (if appropriate); and customer satisfaction rating for each question, and group of questions, such as product quality. When customer comments on recommendations for organizational improvement are collected, they should be logically grouped together along with an indication of how many customers (or what percentage of respondents) made a similar recommendation (this should subsequently be used for prioritizing corrective actions).

This phase should end with an immediate acknowledgment to the customer satisfaction respondents. Respondents should be thanked for their time for completing the survey, and they should be advised on the planned next steps that the organization will take to address the survey findings, including a promise of future communication to inform them of the planned corrective actions. Such an acknowledgment may be sent by a simple postcard or by a letter signed by the organization's management representative.

3. *Analysis and corrective action planning.* Once the customer satisfaction survey results have been compiled, an initial presentation may be arranged to share the results of the survey with senior management personnel. This may help in obtaining senior management input and support for required resources and personnel for corrective action planning and implementation. Root cause analysis and corrective action planning should be conducted by including the appropriate departments that are involved in the specific item or process being assessed. The established corrective action plan should be time-bound, with clear assignment of responsibility for each action. This exercise should be facilitated by the quality department, and analysis techniques such as those discussed in explanation of subclause 8.2.3 should be used.

4. *Results reporting and corrective action implementation.* Once the survey results have been analyzed and a time-bound corrective action plan

has been formulated, the information should be communicated to senior management to secure their approval for the planned corrective actions. The survey results and planned corrective actions should also be shared with employees. This is because employee participation is essential in implementing the corrective actions. By being made aware of the survey results and causes of observed problems, employees will be better able to understand the need to change their processes and documentation in accordance with the corrective action plan. Note that this employee communication also serves as an example to demonstrate conformance with employee communication requirements in subclause 5.5.3. A summary of the survey results and associated corrective action plans should also be shared with the customers. This helps positively reinforce that the organization is committed to improving customer satisfaction levels and is taking specific steps to address the results of the survey. Furthermore, it serves as an example to demonstrate conformance to customer communication requirements in subclause 7.2.3.

Corrective action implementation progress must be continually monitored, and implementation progress must be reviewed at periodic management reviews of the QMS (as per subclause 5.6.2). Such status reporting to senior management helps ensure that all departments accord high priority to their respective tasks due to senior management awareness of their progress, or lack thereof. Moreover, it enables timely management intervention if the implementation of the corrective action plan starts to fall behind schedule.

5. *Follow-up.* This is the final phase in the customer satisfaction process and it closes the loop on the implemented corrective actions by verifying the effectiveness of the implemented corrective actions in achieving planned results. For this purpose, the results from the next customer satisfaction survey should be analyzed to ascertain whether there has been improvement from previously reported satisfaction levels. If for a particular item or process, corrective actions were implemented yet there is no improvement in customer satisfaction, or in fact customer satisfaction has regressed, then additional corrective actions would typically be needed to supplement those already implemented. This may require a reanalysis of the problem root causes and needed remedial action.

Subclause 8.2.2: Internal audit

This subclause states that the organization must conduct internal audits at planned intervals to verify that the QMS implementation is adequate and effective. Internal audits must verify that the QMS implementation conforms to applicable requirements of ISO 9001:2000, the QMS requirements of the organization, and the organization's product realization processes. Further, the audits must verify that the QMS is maintained and is not allowed to fall into a state of disrepair.

This subclause also requires that in planning the audit program, consideration must be given to past audit results, and the current state and importance of the processes and areas to be audited. Such audit criteria must be specified along with scope of audits, frequency, and audit methods. To ensure objectivity and impartiality, the auditors must be independent of the areas being audited, and they must not audit their own work. The responsibilities and requirements that pertain to audit planning and execution, and reporting of audit results and maintenance of audit records, must be specified in a documented procedure. Finally, management personnel responsible for the area audited must ensure that all corrective actions are implemented in a timely fashion, as agreed upon with the auditor. The auditor must subsequently verify and report on the results of the corrective action verification.

In order to conform to the aforementioned requirements, it is best to address them in the organization's internal audits procedure, the documentation of which is specifically required by this subclause. Following is a list of key items[2] that should be addressed in the internal audits procedure:

1. *Types of internal audits.* The organization should identify what types of internal audits, also called first-party audits, need to be performed.[3] Depending on the object being audited, the audit may be a process audit, that is, audit to process definition; project audit, that is, audit to project plan(s); or a product audit, that is, audit to product specification(s). Some organizations also use the term *system audit* or *QMS audit,* which is simply an audit of all processes within the scope of the QMS.

The overall audit approach should be clarified, that is, will the audits be performed on a requirements clause basis, or on a department basis? The former entails a verification of all work performed in the scope of a requirements clause—this work may span multiple departments; the latter entails a verification of all activities performed within a department—this work may span multiple requirements clauses and processes. An organization may choose either approach, based on its preference.

2. *High-level audit planning.* For each type of internal audit, the procedure should also identify which department in the organization is responsible for performing the audit. Internal audits are typically performed by the organization's quality department, but they may be performed by other personnel as long as the following two conditions are met: the person

performing the audit is trained and qualified as a quality auditor, and is independent of the area being audited. That is, personnel cannot formally audit their own work or their own department.

Insofar as auditor training is concerned, most ISO 9000 registrars offer QMS auditor training courses certified by reputed international bodies, such as the International Register of Certified Auditors (IRCA) and the International Auditor and Training Certification Association (IATCA).

At the beginning of the year, an annual internal audit schedule should be prepared that lists the audits planned for each month of the year. Such an audit schedule may be a simple spreadsheet with separate columns for each month of the year and separate rows for each audit planned. At the same time, the internal audits procedure should include provisions to allow unannounced (or "surprise") audits, if necessary.

The procedure should list the considerations and criteria that are to be used in establishing the annual audit schedule. Such considerations and criteria may include but are not limited to:

a. Requirement that each clause of ISO 9001:2000 be audited at least once a year. Note that when the QMS is newly established, more frequent audits are typically required.

b. Requirement that critical areas of the SPDP and areas of weakness (as determined from past audits) be audited at least twice a year.

c. Consideration should be given to not scheduling internal audits during peak holiday and vacation times of the year.

d. Consideration should be given to scheduling a near-term audit of areas that have undergone recent change. This may include changes in operating process(es) and procedure(s), significant employee turnover, changes in departmental responsibilities, or other such factors.

e. For organizations that are or intend to be formally registered to ISO 9000, consideration should be given to not scheduling internal audits at times that conflict with the audit schedule of the registrar.

Insofar as the auditing strategy is concerned, project audits should sample various projects and should verify whether project execution conforms to project requirements and project plans. It is not necessary, and typically not feasible, to audit all the phases and processes in any one project, unless the project is complete or close to completion. Therefore, it is acceptable to audit *different* projects at *different* stages of execution. If the project(s) selected to be audited are behind schedule, the auditor may reschedule the audit or select an alternate project.

As the due date for a scheduled audit draws closer, reasonable advance notice should be provided to the management personnel of the areas to be audited by means of a formal audit plan. It is desirable to release such an audit plan at least one month before the planned audit date(s). The audit plan should contain information such as: objectives and scope of the audit; areas to be audited; date(s) of the audit; lead auditor for the audit; and other pertinent information. It is worthwhile to emphasize in this notification that the purpose of the audit is to assess processes, products, or projects (as the case may be), and the audit *must not* be viewed as personnel assessment. Management personnel should be requested to confirm that the proposed audit dates are acceptable and that there are no special circumstances that necessitate rescheduling. If an audit involves travel to another site, then, if appropriate, travel arrangements should be initiated at this time.

In addition to planning for internal audits to be conducted by the quality department, the organization should also plan for an audit of its internal audit program and of the quality department. Such an audit must be performed by personnel other than those responsible for the internal audit program. Some organizations engage the services of outside quality consultants to perform such an audit.

3. *Detailed audit planning.* Prior to an audit, the auditor(s) should prepare for the audit by reviewing relevant ISO 9001:2000 requirements, QMS documentation, and project documentation. The auditor(s) should review relevant past audit reports, and internal corrective and preventive action records to ensure past problems are not recurring, and to identify outstanding problems that need to be followed up on during the audit. Measurement data and trends should be reviewed to identify issues that need to be investigated during the audit. In the case of project audits, customer-specific contractual obligations should be reviewed and the audit should verify that the obligations are being met. The auditor should include all identified items for investigation in a formal audit checklist. Audit checklists serve as an invaluable tool to structure the audit interview(s) and ensure adequate coverage of all identified questions.

At least two weeks prior to the audit, an audit notification should be sent to the respective department management personnel providing information on the exact times that the audit will be conducted, purpose and scope of the audit, specific employees requested for the audit (if appropriate), reserved meeting room(s) for the audit (if any), and other relevant information. The audit notification should be accompanied by audit checklists for distribution to the department personnel. Such a practice helps promote acceptance of audits as a means for free and open sharing of information with the auditor for continuous improvement—this, as opposed to promoting a feeling of apprehension and discomfort by auditing employees with secret audit checklists kept close to the auditor's chest. It therefore helps make internal audits nonthreatening to the employees and puts them at ease during the audit interviews.

4. *Audit execution.* When appropriate, the internal audit should commence with a brief opening meeting with the management personnel and employees from the department to be audited. The purpose and scope of the audit should be clarified along with clarification of how the audit will be performed, audit times and breaks, meeting rooms, and time and place for the closing meeting where the audit results will be presented. Meeting attendees should also be given an opportunity to ask questions. When such a meeting is held, a list of meeting participants should be maintained, along with notes from the meeting.

There are three generally accepted methods for conducting an audit: audit interviews, observation of activities, and examination of objective evidence such as process outputs and supporting documentation. When sampling objective evidence, a sample size of three to five is typically recommended. In conducting the audit, the internal auditor should bear in mind that it is generally accepted that conducting internal audits can be and is usually a difficult task because the internal auditors are auditing fellow workers. Some resistance and a certain amount of defensive posturing are natural and expected when people are faced with a situation wherein their work methods and output are evaluated. The auditor should not in any way intimidate the auditee or behave in a way that would reinforce a negative attitude toward the audit. Audit questions should be open-ended, context-specific, or investigatory, as opposed to closed-ended or tricky. Auditor should keep adequate notes from the audits. The auditor should verify that internal audits expected to be conducted by other departments, such as product physical configuration audit and functional configuration audit, are indeed being performed.

Once a nonconformance is identified during an audit, the auditor should share it with the auditee and ensure that the auditee understands the nonconformance. Identification of the severity of a noted nonconformance may be performed outside of the audit interview because it may require further examination of evidence and consultation with other audit team members.

Typically, organizations classify noted nonconformances as *major* or *minor*. A major nonconformance may arise due to:

- A serious deficiency that would adversely affect the quality of the product or service

- A significant nonconformance against requirement(s) contained in ISO 9001:2000 or the organization's QMS that indicates a complete absence or breakdown of compliance to the requirement(s)

- Evidence of systemwide deficiencies

A minor nonconformance is an observed temporary omission, for example, an isolated case of nonconformance with a specific requirement or a minor discrepancy from a stated requirement. Because evidence of systemwide deficiencies constitutes a major finding, this means that if in a certain clause of ISO 9001:2000 or a certain QMS process, the organization has several minor findings, then such minor findings have a serious *cumulative* effect and they may therefore be grouped together under a single major finding. Organizations generally use a third classification called an *observation* to identify a potential problem, or an opportunity for improvement. In all cases, nonconformances and observations should be supported with objective evidence. Additionally, the auditor may record positive observations to recognize observed best practices that management personnel may evaluate for appropriateness for use in other parts of the organization.

This phase should conclude with a closing meeting with the management personnel from the area(s) audited. At this meeting, the results from the audit should be presented, along with a commentary on the overall health of the audited area(s). It is preferable to provide formally documented nonconformances and observations at the closing meeting. (Refer to the corrective action request form in appendix B.) The auditor should identify the due date by when a time-bound corrective action plan from the auditee(s) is requested, and the plan, once received, should be reviewed by the auditor for acceptance. The attendees of the closing meeting should also be informed regarding when the audit report will be formally issued, and the planned next steps for corrective action planning and implementation. Generally, the audit report should be issued within two to four weeks of performing the audit. As with the opening meeting, a list of meeting attendees should be maintained, along with notes from the meeting. Finally, as required by subclause 5.6.2, a summary of the audit results must also be presented at the management review meeting.

5. *Audit reporting.* The purpose of the audit report is to accurately describe the audit and its results. Typical contents of an audit report include the following:

- Brief description of purpose and scope of the audit

- Pertinent details from the audit plan

- Overall statement of adequacy and effectiveness of the areas audited

- Audit outcome (including summary of audit findings)

- List of attendees at the opening meeting and summary of what was discussed

- List of attendees at the closing meeting and summary of what was discussed

- Appendixes with formally documented nonconformances and observations

The audit report should also describe those nonconformances that were discovered during the audit and resolved during the course of the audit with a satisfactory corrective action. The audit report should be provided to the management personnel of the areas audited, and it should be shared with the auditees as well. The internal audits procedure should specify the retention time and location of all audit records, such as the annual audit schedule, audit plans, audit checklists, and audit reports.

6. *Audit follow-up and closure.* Once the auditees have implemented the agreed corrective and/or preventive action(s) within the agreed time frame, the auditor must verify that the implemented action(s) adequately and effectively address the identified root cause(s) of the problem. Nonconformances and observations may be closed upon examination of new objective evidence that demonstrates that the problem has been resolved, or by conducting a reaudit of the affected areas. Once all previously noted nonconformances and observations have been resolved, the audit report can be formally closed. In accordance with requirements of subclause 5.6.2, progress or lack thereof in implementation of corrective and preventive actions must be reported at the periodic management reviews.

At all times, the department performing the audit should maintain up-to-date information on the status of each audit performed and monitor that all audit-related activities are being completed within required time frames.

Subclause 8.2.3: Monitoring and measurement of processes

This subclause requires the organization to monitor and measure QMS processes to verify that the established processes are achieving corresponding objectives. When these objectives are not met, then appropriate corrective action must be undertaken.

In addition to the use of internal audits for the purpose of monitoring adequacy and effectiveness of QMS processes, process execution should be monitored in real time by the process owner, practitioners, and the quality department to ensure that processes are yielding desired results. That is, while executing a process, if difficulties are encountered or deficiencies are observed in the process, then appropriate corrective or preventive action must be taken.

Compliance to measurements requirements in this subclause and in subclause 8.2.4 requires the organization to establish the capability to collect process, project, and product measurements. This in turn requires the establishment of a measurements infrastructure. Use of measurements is central to any process-based improvement approach, and the establishment of organizational processes is an essential prerequisite for process measurements. After all, how would one know what to measure in a process if the process itself is undefined? As stated earlier in this book, the concept of process-based improvement forms the underpinnings of ISO 9001:2000. It follows that, for continuous process improvement, the current capability of a process must be known. Process measurements help quantify the current capability of a process, and the desired capability of a process. Similarly, product measurements help quantify the current quality of a product, and the desired quality of a product. Due to these reasons, measurements requirements are now included as a separate requirements subclause in ISO 9001:2000.

An organization's measurements infrastructure includes the complete framework, methods, and tools for collection of measurements, so that the identified measures are grounded in sound measurement practices and yield measurement data that are objective and useful. Following is a list of key items that should be addressed in establishing a corporate measurements infrastructure (see Figure 8.1, page 189):

• *Measurement item.* The measurement item is the entity that is being evaluated by means of measurements to identify opportunities for improvement. The measurement item may be the organization itself, or processes, projects, or products. An example of a framework for organizational measurement is the balanced scorecard approach.[4] Process measurements are used for monitoring and improving QMS processes, and product measurements are used for monitoring and improving product quality. Project measurements are required because, in the context of software development, processes are not executed in a vacuum but within the bounds of a software development project. Project measures complement process measures and they are useful during project execution for real-time project tracking and control, and for conducting project post-mortem analysis to identify future process improvements. Note that sometimes the same metric may belong to more than one metric type: process, project, or product metric.

• *Goal–question–metric approach to metrics identification.* The goal–question–metric (GQM) approach to identifying metrics is based on the premise that for metrics to be purposeful, they should be derived in a top-down fashion.[5] That is, first a measurement goal or purpose should be determined, and then a set of questions should be asked to further define or characterize the measurement goal. This is followed by identification of metrics to support each question. Sometimes the measurement goal may be derived by decomposition of a higher-level goal, as in the case of management by objectives techniques where high-level organizational goals are decomposed at lower levels of the organization. Also, bear in mind that an organization collects measurements for use by different users, such as senior management, project manager(s), process owners, engineers, quality department personnel, and customers. Therefore, in determining what characteristics need to be measured and what metrics to use, consideration should be given to addressing the needs of various types of users who would be interested in a specific measurement. The following example is provided to illustrate the GQM approach:

Say an organization identifies the following high-level goal (G): Improve project planning. Then, a valid set of questions to help characterize project planning would be:

Q1. What is the current accuracy of estimating a project schedule?

Q2. What is the current accuracy of estimating project effort?

Q3. How does the actual cost of project execution compare with the projected cost?

For each of these questions, the following corresponding project metrics can be identified (refer to next subsection "Measurement Logistics" for further guidance on metrics definition):

M1. Planning precision (PP): $100 - 100 \times |$ (planned lead time – actual lead time)/planned lead time $| = \%$

Note: If PP is negative, it is set to zero. This happens when actual lead time $> 2 \times$ planned lead time

M2. Effort estimation (EE): $100 - 100 \times |$ (planned effort – actual effort)/planned effort $| = \%$

Note: Measurement unit for effort is person-hours. If EE is negative, it is set to zero. This happens when actual effort $> 2 \times$ planned effort

M3. Cost performance index (CPI): actual cost of work performed/budgeted cost of work performed

Note: CPI = 1 (project is within budget); CPI > 1 (project is over budget); CPI < 1 (project is under budget)

Measurement Logistics

• *Metrics definition.* It is recommended that each of the identified metrics possess certain desirable characteristics. The identified metrics should be useful and accepted as a good indicator of the characteristic being measured. The metric should be precisely defined, simple to understand, and relatively easy to compute. The measurement unit for the metric should also be defined and consistently applied.

• *Primitive data collection method and tools.* Most metrics are derived metrics as opposed to primitive metrics. That is, the final measurement value is computed (derived) from certain primitive data. For example, computation of planning precision requires that primitive data on the planned lead time and actual lead time be collected. Therefore, for each identified metric, the method and tools for collecting the necessary primitive data should be specified. If an automated tool is used for measurement computation, it should be placed under configuration control, secured from unauthorized access, and backed up for disaster recovery. The measurement unit for the primitive data should also be defined and consistently applied.

• *Rules for computing measurements.* The computation of the measurement value, hereafter referred to as *measurement data*, should be free from personal interpretation and subjectivity. Measurement data that has been compromised, either intentionally or unintentionally (due to lack of defined rules for computing it), will render it inaccurate, worthless, and open to discussion. Therefore, all dos and don'ts associated with computing measurement data should be established and agreed upon with appropriate parties.

• *Measurement data storage.* Measurement data should preferably be stored in a centralized measurements repository or database; however, such a database may also be substituted by a collection of databases. The storage location for each measurement data should be established and communicated to appropriate parties. To aid measurement data analysis, it is desirable that the database allows querying of measurement data based on selected parameters.

• *Measurement data reporting.* Guidelines should be established on how often measurement data are to be reported, who reports them and to whom, and how they are to be reported. Reported measurement data should generally be supported by a trend and causal analysis of the data. When the recorded data deviates from the established upper and lower control limits (in the case of a control chart), or falls below a predetermined target value, remedial steps should be taken by means of appropriate corrective, preventive, and improvement actions.

• *Roles and responsibilities.* Roles and responsibilities should be identified for all activities within the measurements infrastructure, beginning with identification of and agreement on required metrics, and ending with analysis of measurement data for future improvements. When the responsibility to collect primitive data is distributed among various departments in the organization, then the responsibility for ensuring cross-functional consistency in measurement practices should be assigned to one department. Typically, this role is fulfilled by the organization's quality department.

• *Training.* Training and ongoing consulting support should be provided to all personnel involved in identifying needed metrics, collecting primitive data, computing measurements, reporting, and analyzing measurement data. This includes training on use of quality tools for data analysis, which is described next.

Analyze Measurement Data for Future Improvements

• *Analyze current measurement data.* Once the measurements have been computed, they must be analyzed, both for trends as well as for reasons behind a particular trend or deviation from control limits or target values. There are various quality tools available that can be used for data representation and analysis, such as control charts, run charts, scatter diagrams, Pareto charts, Ishikawa (or fishbone) diagrams, tree diagrams, and affinity diagrams.[6] For example, say a process metric is used to record the type of defects identified in software code reviews. Once the total number of defects of each type is computed for all the software code reviews held, the data can be presented and analyzed using a Pareto chart to identify the vital few defect types that are most frequently encountered. By focusing corrective action on these frequently observed defects, and if these defects are also the most significant, one can reduce the number and severity of defects found in software code reviews.

• *Determine SMART target value(s).* As described earlier, the basic premise of the GQM approach to metrics identification is that in order to identify metrics, there has to be measurement goal. It follows that once the metric has been identified, in order to improve performance from current levels or to maintain performance within certain bounds, the original qualitative measurement goal has to be quantified in terms of the specific metrics identified. To maintain performance within certain bounds, organizations typically use control charts with specific upper and lower control limits derived from past data—a mechanism that is known as *statistical process control.* However, when process or product improvements are to be achieved, then a new target value needs to be identified. The new target value should possess the SMART characteristics described earlier in this book. To ensure that an established target value possesses SMART characteristics, the target value should be identified by involving the appropriate employees and departments, as opposed to being arbitrarily determined and foisted upon them. For example, the original qualitative measurement goal of "G: Improve project planning" discussed earlier in this section may now be supported by underlying quantitative goals such as:

G1:   Improve planning precision from the current value of 70 percent to 80 percent by the end of next calendar year.

G2:   Improve effort estimation from the current value of 60 percent to 75 percent by the end of next calendar year.

G3:   Improve cost performance index from the current value of 1.25 to 1.15 by the end of next calendar year.

The identified target values should be deployed within the organization by tying them to individual and team annual performance objectives, when appropriate. Employees should be provided reward-based incentives to achieve the identified target value for each metric. Team rewards should be used when the attainment of target values requires intra- and inter-teamwork collaboration. The aforementioned approach helps emphasize the importance of the identified goals and drives employees to achieve those goals, thus increasing the likelihood of success. However, care should be taken to ensure that the identified goals are balanced goals that do not merely promote the achievement of a specific objective at the expense of quality and other considerations. For example, a measurement goal of 90 percent on-time product delivery will invariably be at the expense of quality considerations unless there are complementary quality goals that must be met and there are in-built accountability mechanisms in the reward system to preclude the organization from persistently delivering an inferior quality product on time (where the quality goals for a product release have a semblance of having been met, but customer-reported defects and experiences with the product contradict organizational claims about the true quality of the product). As an example of an accountability mechanism, critical product failures immediately after release may cause an on-time product delivery to be counted as a late delivery.

• *Identify improvement actions.* In order to facilitate the achievement of the new target value, specific improvement actions must be identified and assigned to responsible personnel. Without the identification of improvement actions, realization of the target value is unlikely to materialize, because the current process will only result in achievement of current performance levels. Similarly, when the performance deviates from established control limits, appropriate corrective actions should be identified by means such as Ishikawa diagrams (for identifying root cause) and tree diagrams (for identifying means to address the identified root cause).

Sample Process and Project Metrics

Table 8.1 lists some process metrics that an organization may use for process improvement. Table 8.2 lists some project metrics that an organization may use for project planning, tracking, and control.

Subclause 8.2.4: Monitoring and measurement of product

This subclause requires the organization to monitor and measure the characteristics of the product to verify that product requirements have been met. This must be performed at appropriate times in accordance with the established SDLC.

ISO 90003 clarifies that means to monitor and measure product conformity to requirements includes reviews, verification, and validation activities. Each of these activities was explained in related subclauses 7.3.4, 7.3.5, and 7.3.6. Measurement of product conformity requires use of the organization's measurements infrastructure to identify product metrics and target values, collect measurement data, and analyze measurement data for required corrective, preventive, and improvement actions (refer to previous discussion under explanation of subclause 8.2.3).

Table 8.1   Sample process metrics.

Process Metric	Metric Definition	
	Explanation	**Computation**
Defect detection effectiveness (also referred to as defect removal effectiveness)	A measure of the effectiveness of defect detection derived by comparing number of defects detected during product testing versus number of defects that escaped.	Number of defects detected in a test activity *divided by* the *sum of* the number of defects detected during the test activity and the number of defects detected after completion of the test activity. For example, system test effectiveness = defects found in system test/(defects found in system test + defects found in acceptance test + defects found during operational use of the product by the customer)[7] *Note:* Organizational defect detection effectiveness can be computed by dividing all defects found in-house prior to release of the product by the sum of all defects found prior to release of the product and after release of the product.[8]
Mean age of open customer-reported defects	A measure of responsiveness to the customer computed in terms of the mean age of customer-reported defects that remained open at the end of a month. *Note:* Similarly, the mean age of customer-reported defects closed in a month can be computed. This metric is also referred to as the total turnaround time, or mean time to change (MTTC).	Total time customer-reported defects that remained open at the end of the month have been open *divided by* total number of customer-reported defects that remained open at the end of the month.
Initial turnaround time to customer	Another measure of responsiveness to the customer computed in terms of percentage of customer reported defects in a month for which an acceptable workaround was provided within the time frame agreed to with the customer.	Customer-reported defects for a month for which an acceptable workaround was provided within the agreed time frame *divided by* total number of customer-reported defects in the month.

Continued

Continued

Process Metric	Metric Definition	
	Explanation	**Computation**
Root cause of injected defects	A measure of the most frequently occurring causes for software defects.	Number of defects attributed to a set of predetermined root causes, such as missing/incorrect requirement, incorrect design, code bug—uninitialized parameter, code bug—logic error, and so on.
Cost of rework	Measure of the effort expended in a project in rework.	Amount of time expended, typically in person-hours, for performing rework in a specific project phase. *Note:* To enable tracking of this metric, it is required that all rework effort be charged to separate time-reporting codes reserved for rework performed under each project phase.

Table 8.2 Sample project metrics.

Project Metric	Metric Definition	
	Explanation	**Computation**
Planning precision	Accuracy of estimating project schedule	100 *minus* 100 *multiplied by* ABS [(planned lead time *minus* actual lead time) *divided by* planned lead time]
Effort estimation	Accuracy of estimating project effort	100 *minus* 100 *multiplied* by ABS [(planned effort *minus* actual effort) *divided by* planned effort]
Productivity	A measure of the product size developed and the associated effort expended	Product size in lines of source code[9] *divided by* effort expended (typically, in person-hours).
Cost performance index	Assessment of variance of cost of project execution from budgeted cost of project execution	Actual cost of work performed *divided by* budgeted cost of work performed.
Activity and phase lead times	The actual time in calendar days used for performing an activity or phase	Activity or phase end date *minus* the start date.

Continued

Continued

Project Metric	Metric Definition	
	Explanation	**Computation**
Milestone slippage	The number of project milestones failing to achieve the predefined milestone criteria or due date.	Number of failed milestones *divided by* total number of project milestones.
Baseline deliverable quality[10]	The quality of deliverables included in a formal CM baseline.	Number of baseline deliverables inspected *divided by* total number of baseline deliverables required to be inspected.
Requirements change	Ongoing metric illustrating requirements instability during project execution.	Ongoing cumulative count of newly added and modified requirements, plotted against weeks or months of project execution.
Requirements slippage[11]	The number of requirements slipped (not implemented) in the project.	Number of slipped requirements *divided by* total number of project requirements
Functionality correctness[12]	The percentage of functional requirements correctly implemented in the project.	Number of correctly implemented functional requirements confirmed during system test *divided by* the total number of functional requirements for the product release.
Number and severity of outstanding defects	Severity and count of defects in the product outstanding at any given time in a project. These are typically found in internal test activities, such as unit, integration, and system test.	Total number of outstanding defects in the product prior to release (ordered by severity).

Table 8.3 lists some product metrics that an organization may use for measuring product quality.

This subclause also requires that evidence of product conformance to acceptance criteria be maintained. A record of who authorized product release is also required. Also, the product and service delivery must not proceed until the acceptance criteria have been met, and deviations, if any, have been approved by a relevant authority, and when appropriate, by the customer.

In order to comply with this requirement, first of all, product acceptance criteria should be unambiguously established and communicated to appropriate employees. Establishment of acceptance criteria was explained

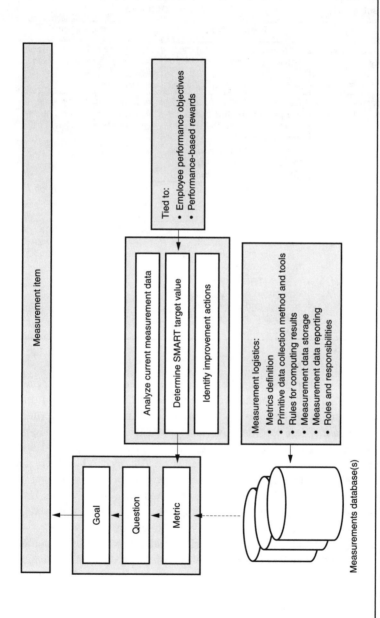

Figure 8.1 Key elements of a measurements infrastructure.

Table 8.3 Sample product metrics.

Product Metric	Metric Definition	
	Explanation	**Computation**
Software defect density	Normalized number of software defects.	Number of software defects *divided by* product size in thousands of lines of source code.[13]
Customer-reported defects	Count of defects found in the product by the customer in any given month. This includes defects found during and after acceptance testing (that is, during deployment and use).	Total number of customer-reported defects in a month (ordered by severity).
Software reliability	Rate of software failures[14] over time.	Number of failures *divided by* total time of the product in use.
Mean time between failure (MTBF)	Time elapsed between failures of the product. Typically measured in days, hours, or minutes.

Note: MTBF may be computed during product testing, and it may be computed after product release. | Sum of the all the times elapsed between failures *divided by* the total number of failures. |

in chapter 7. Acceptable records to demonstrate conformance to acceptance criteria include acceptance test report(s) and test records; and minutes of meeting(s) held to review the product against acceptance criteria prior to release. These records must clearly indicate what criteria were not met, and such unsatisfied acceptance criteria should be supported with associated risk identification, and mitigation (if any). When there are unsatisfied acceptance criteria that may cause a prior customer commitment or contractual commitment to be breached, then the deviation must be reviewed in advance with the customer for acceptance, followed by identification and execution of needed corrective action(s).

The QMS documentation should clearly identify the relevant authority that is responsible for authorizing release of the product, and there must be supporting documentation available to demonstrate that product releases were indeed authorized for release by the identified relevant authority. For example, signature or electronic approval by the relevant authority is acceptable as a release authorization record.

CLAUSE 8.3: CONTROL OF NONCONFORMING PRODUCT

This clause states that a product that does not conform to its requirements must be identified and controlled to prevent its unintended use or delivery. Following are acceptable ways of dealing with a product nonconformance found prior to or after release to the customer:

1. Take corrective action to eliminate the identified nonconformity. Note that in this case, the corrected product must be verified to ensure the nonconformity does not exist, and no new nonconformity has been introduced.

2. Allow use or delivery of the product after securing approval from the appropriate authority in the organization, and when appropriate, from the customer.

3. Take suitable action to prevent the original intended use of the product.

In the context of the software industry, identification and control of nonconforming product is accomplished by means of CM and defect management practices. The identification, authorization, tracking, and reporting of all required corrective actions as a result of a reported defect were discussed in the explanation of CM and the CCB in subclause 7.5.3, and, therefore, are not repeated here. If a reported defect is of low severity, determined to be of minimal risk, and within the organization's permissible number of latent defects in a product release, the CCB may authorize that the defect fix be deferred to a future product release. In other words, every reported defect need not and typically cannot be resolved in the next immediate release of the product. However, when appropriate, the customer should be informed in advance to confirm that there is no adverse impact on the customer due to a known defect, and to obtain concession to ship the product with the known defect. If a viable workaround exists, it should be provided to the customer in order to alleviate the problem. Alternatively, if appropriate and acceptable to the customer, access to the defective functionality may be disabled or restricted to preclude its unintentional use. When firmware or embedded software is determined to be defective, the subject hardware may need to be physically marked as nonconforming and segregated in order to preclude its delivery to the customer.

Finally, this clause states that there must be a documented procedure that describes the process and associated responsibilities and authorities for controlling a nonconforming product. Also, records of the nature of non-conformities and subsequent action must be maintained.

In order to comply with this requirement, the organization's defect management process, key elements of which were described under explanation of subclause 7.5.3, should be documented in a procedure. This procedure should also specify the records that need to be maintained during the process. Such record keeping is generally automated because organizations use COTS defect or change management software tools to store all required information on each product defect—including information on a defect and its audit trail through resolution.

CLAUSE 8.4: ANALYSIS OF DATA

This clause states that the organization must identify, collect, and analyze appropriate monitoring and measurement data to demonstrate suitability and effectiveness of the QMS, and to identify opportunities for improvement.

Compliance to these requirements can be achieved by following the guidance provided under explanation of subclause 8.2.3 for collection of primitive data, and computation and analysis of process, project, and product measurements. The analysis of process, project, and product measurement data yields valuable information on the suitability and effectiveness of current practices in the QMS, and opportunities for improvement.

This clause also requires that the data analysis provide information pertaining to conformance of the product to requirements, characteristics and trends of products and processes, customer satisfaction, and supplier performance.

Examples of metrics that can be analyzed to assess product conformance to requirements, and to assess characteristics and trends of products and processes were discussed under explanation of subclauses 8.2.3 and 8.2.4. Insofar as customer satisfaction is concerned, this requirements clause complements requirements subclause 8.2.1 by requiring that the collected customer satisfaction data be analyzed for future improvements. The type of customer satisfaction data an organization collects is dictated by the questions included in the organization's customer satisfaction survey. As stated earlier, the content of customer satisfaction surveys varies from one organization to the other, although there may be some common elements. Therefore, as a whole, the type of customer satisfaction data collected by one software development organization will differ from that collected by another software development organization. In other words, there are no generally accepted measures of customer satisfaction in the software industry.

Nevertheless, an organization should analyze its customer satisfaction data as per guidance provided in explanation of subclause 8.2.3.

Finally, the organization must track the performance of its supplier(s) with the help of quality metrics. Summary of supplier performance data should be presented at the periodic management review meetings to ensure continued management awareness of supplier performance, and for discussion of related quality concerns. Establishment of certain supplier quality metrics may require consultations with the supplier(s). This is because the quality metrics may entail the collection of certain measurement data by the supplier, in accordance with agreed measurement methods and tools. All suppliers should be required to periodically report their data, as needed, to the organization for the agreed quality metrics. Examples of quality metrics that may be used to monitor ongoing supplier performance include use of suitable process, project, and product measurements. For example, defect detection effectiveness of the supplier = defects found by the supplier prior to product release to the organization/(defects found by the supplier prior to product release to the organization + defects found in acceptance test by the organization + defects found during operational use of the product by the end customer and attributed to the supplier)

CLAUSE 8.5: IMPROVEMENT

Subclause 8.5.1: Continual improvement

This subclause requires the organization to continually improve the effectiveness of its QMS by means of its quality policy, quality objectives, audit results, analysis of measurement data, corrective and preventive actions, and management review of the QMS.

This is a critical subclause that embodies the now explicit continual improvement intent of ISO 9001:2000. It ties together each of the essential tools of continual improvement discussed in previous clauses: quality policy, quality objectives, audit results, analysis of measurement data, corrective and preventive actions, and management review of the QMS. It requires that organizations not merely maintain status quo but demonstrate improvements in efficiency and effectiveness of their QMS. In order to determine what an organization can do to demonstrate compliance with this requirement, it is perhaps preferable to examine what the external auditor (representing the registrar) would look for in auditing this requirement. The external auditor can examine several pieces of evidence to assess compliance to this requirement. For example, the external auditor may examine whether, over a period of time, the organization's quality objectives reflect a gradual raising of the bar with regard to expected results (when appropriate).[15] Further, the external auditor may examine whether measurement data trends confirm a gradual improvement in performance levels (in accordance with the quality objectives), or they merely indicate stagnation in performance levels. The external auditor may examine internal audit reports to ascertain whether internal auditors merely focus on compliance auditing, or whether they also assess deficiencies in process effectiveness and opportunities for improvement. The auditor may also examine if the organization is able to provide examples of continual improvement as evidenced by corrective[16] and preventive action records (refer to subclauses 8.5.2 and 8.5.3). If the organization has an adequately functioning process for periodic management review of the QMS and associated records (as per subclause 5.6.3), then it serves as evidence that management personnel are driving and overseeing continual improvements in the organization.

ISO 90003 provides the additional guidance that in order to comply with this requirement, organizations should consider establishing a generic improvement process with the following key elements: process definition, process assessment, and process improvement. In fact, use of such an improvement process is intrinsic to each of the improvement tools described earlier in this section—they all require that the process be defined[17]; the process either be quantitatively or qualitatively assessed; and be analyzed to identify opportunities for improvement. This process analysis may be performed informally or using formal techniques such as those described in explanation of subclause 8.2.3.

In summary, to comply with this requirement, the organization has to use each of the aforementioned tools to improve performance beyond current levels. Improvements may be quantitative, such as with the use of metrics, or they may be qualitative, such as with the use of corrective and preventive actions and other means described in this section.

Subclause 8.5.2: Corrective action

This subclause states that when a nonconformance is found, then the organization must take appropriate corrective action to eliminate the root cause of the nonconformance. A procedure must be formally documented to clarify requirements pertaining to:

- Review of nonconformances (including customer complaints)
- Identification of root cause(s) of each nonconformance
- Determination of whether a corrective action(s) is required

- Identification and timely implementation of appropriate corrective action(s) that effectively eliminates the root cause(s) of each nonconformance

- Recording of the results of the corrective action(s)

- Review of the implemented corrective action(s)

First, it needs to be clarified that, in the context of this requirements subclause, a nonconformance is not limited to an audit finding only. A nonconformance includes but is not limited to:

- Failure during process execution to comply with stated process requirements

- Failure of the product to comply with product requirements

- Failure of the organization in meeting reasonable customer expectations (which result in a valid customer complaint)

- Observed discrepancy or errors in any type of documentation—process, project, or product documentation

A nonconformance may be detected during an audit (internal or external), or outside of an audit—in the normal course of business. In both cases, most organizations employ a common mechanism for handling process-related nonconformances:

1. The observed nonconformance is recorded by the auditor (typically the quality department) in a corrective action request form (refer to appendix B). Note that a nonconformance may also be identified by an ordinary employee and then handed off to the quality department for further action.

2. The respective department (or personnel) against which the nonconformance is reported, responds with a root cause analysis and proposed corrective action, which is reviewed by the auditor for concurrence. It must be ensured that the proposed corrective action directly addresses the identified root cause(s) of the problem with the intent to not only immediately correct the noted problem, but also to *prevent* recurrence of the nonconformance in the future.[18] At this time, both parties also agree on the time frame within which the corrective action must be implemented. Note that in certain circumstances, it may be agreed that pursuing a corrective action would yield limited or no gains, and therefore, it may be appropriate to not pursue a corrective action. For example, a nonconformance might have been found against a process definition that is already planned to be discontinued or significantly revised. Or, a nonconformance might

have been found long after a process was executed, and correcting the non-conformance now may involve significant costs, with little or no gains. In such a situation, it may be advisable to instead pursue a preventive action for the problem, to preclude its occurrence in the future.

3. The corrective action is then implemented within the agreed time frame, and upon completion, the auditor verifies the records of the implemented corrective action(s). If the corrective action is implemented as originally agreed, the nonconformance is formally closed out.

The aforementioned mechanism, or a similar mechanism, should also be utilized for handling customer complaints as well. In accordance with requirements in subclause 7.2.3, the customer should be kept informed about the status of the customer's complaints.

When a need for corrective action is observed in the software product, it should be handled by means of the defect management process and related CM practices discussed under explanation of subclause 7.5.3.

Subclause 8.5.3: Preventive action

This subclause requires the organization to identify and eliminate the causes of potential nonconformances. The key difference between this subclause and the previous subclause is that this subclause deals with a *potential* nonconformance, that is, a nonconformance that has not yet occurred, while the previous subclause deals with a *known* nonconformance, that is, a nonconformance that has already occurred. As in the previous subclause, this subclause requires that a procedure be formally documented to clarify requirements pertaining to:

- Review of potential nonconformances (including customer complaints)

- Identification of root cause(s) of each potential nonconformance

- Determination of whether a preventive action is required

- Identification and timely implementation of appropriate preventive action(s) that effectively eliminates the root cause(s) of the potential nonconformance

- Recording of the results of the preventive action(s)

- Review of the implemented preventive action(s)

The mechanism for handling potential nonconformances should mimic the mechanism described in the previous section for handling of known nonconformances. However, there is a subtle difference. In reporting a potential nonconformance, the auditor may identify the root cause that is likely to cause a potential nonconformance. This is because, by definition, a potential nonconformance has not yet occurred. However, an astute auditor or employee may be able to anticipate a potential nonconformance from examining a particular situation. The particular situation may itself be the root cause of a potential nonconformance. As with a known nonconformance, the proposed preventive action must effectively address the identified root cause. Once the preventive action has been implemented, the auditor should examine the associated records to verify that actions as previously agreed have been implemented. The potential nonconformance can then be closed out.

When a preventive action is implemented in response to a customer complaint, then the customer should be kept informed about the status of the customer complaint (as per subclause 7.2.3). When a preventive action is required to be implemented in the software product, it should be handled by means of the defect management process and related CM practices discussed under explanation of subclause 7.5.3.

ENDNOTES

1. An organization may also choose to engage the services of a third-party vendor for preparing the survey questionnaire (with organizational input), and for conducting and reporting the survey results.
2. ISO has published a standard, *BSR/ISO/ASQ QE 19011-2002, Guidelines for quality and/or environmental management systems auditing,* that provides guidance on establishing an effective internal audit program.
3. When the organization subcontracts to an outside vendor(s), such as an offshore software developer, then in order to exercise control over its subcontractor(s), the organization should plan for second-party audits of its subcontractor(s). This entails establishing a process for conducting second-party audits.
4. Kaplan, R., and D. Norton, "The Balanced Scorecard: Measures that Drive Performance," *Harvard Business Review* (January 1992).
5. Basili, V., and D. M. Weiss, "A Methodology for Collecting Valid Software Engineering Data." *IEEE Transactions on Software Engineering* 10, no. 3 (November 1984).
6. Foster, T., *Managing Quality: An Integrative Approach* (Englewood Cliffs, NJ: Prentice Hall, 2000).
7. Because customers report defects until the end-of-life of a product, it causes the value of defect detection effectiveness to change until the end-of-life of the product. However, in order to arrive at a reasonably accurate measurement value (without having to wait until the end-of-life of the product), some organizations only count defects reported within a certain amount of time

after release of the product. This time period corresponds to the time frame within which the organization has historically received the majority of customer-reported defects after product release. In identifying this time period, time taken to deploy the organization's product should also be considered, because sometimes the deployment period itself may span a few months as in the case of telecommunication software applications. Depending on an organization's type of product and time-to-deploy, such a time period may be up to six months after product release, or more.

8. According to Capers Jones, world-class organizations have organizational defect detection effectiveness greater than 95 percent (Jones 1995).

9. Some organizations use function points or feature points instead of lines of code as a measure of software size. Explanation of function and feature points is provided in (Pressman 1996).

10. This may also be regarded as a product metric of "maintainability" (Van Veenendaal et al. 2002).

11. This may also be used as a product metric of "functionality" (functional completeness), which can be computed by dividing the number of functional requirements implemented (confirmed during system test) *divided by* the total number of functional requirements for the product release (Van Veenendaal et al. 2002).

12. This may also be regarded as a product metric of "functionality" (functional correctness) (Van Veenendaal et al. 2002).

13. From an annual survey of 1000 global IT companies conducted in 2001, Metricnet and the META group reported that post-release software defect density for U.S. companies was 0.37 defects/KLOC, and for non-U.S. companies was 0.47 defects/KLOC (Rubin et al. 2002).

14. Here, a failure is regarded as a critical defect in the software that causes the software to fail catastrophically—rendering it completely unusable or unreliable, or rendering key functionality unusable or unreliable.

15. It is recognized that depending on the maturity and performance level each process in the QMS has attained, it may not be possible, cost-effective, or otherwise desirable to pursue further improvement for *each* metric. For such metrics, the objective changes to maintaining performance at or above a desired level, or within the bounds of certain acceptable levels—the concept of SPC.

16. By definition, every corrective action does not qualify as an "improvement" action. This is because, in some cases, corrective actions are performed only to correct a discrepancy from stated requirements. Therefore, strictly speaking, in such a case, the corrective action is to force adherence to the stated performance level (that is, maintenance of a performance level), as opposed to *improving* it.

17. Definition does not necessarily imply that the process be documented.

18. As an example, if a certain software defect is found in a product, corrective action planning must not only address the near-term objective of correcting the observed software defect, but it must also address the longer-term objective of preventing similar defects from recurring in the future.

9

ISO 9000
Registration Audit

You have now completed the definition and implementation of your QMS. You have also successfully implemented an internal audits program, and the internal audits have confirmed the growing stability of the newly instituted QMS. Your organization is now ready for the next step—selection of the registrar who will perform the final registration audit to ascertain whether your organization is deserving of the coveted ISO 9000 registration.

How should the registrar selection be performed? Specifically, what process should be followed to select a registrar? What information should be elicited from the registrars? How should the registrar responses be evaluated, that is, what criteria should one use to compare one registrar with another? Should the final selection be based solely on review of some company information provided by the registrar, and telephone conversations with the registrar, or is a face-to-face meeting desirable?

Clearly, the process of selecting a registrar is nontrivial, and the approach adopted may very well determine the quality, experience, and specific domain expertise of the registrar selected. Harmony in the approach and objective of the auditor with the organization's ultimate objectives in pursuing a registration is vital, not only for achieving the tactical objective of the registration itself, but more importantly, for realizing the longer-term objective of instituting continuous process improvement. A good ISO 9000 auditor is one who has earned the respect and acceptance of his or her clients by adding value to their quality improvement effort. Such an auditor firmly believes in the value of audits in not only verifying compliance to ISO 9000 requirements but also in continuous process improvement. Therefore, such an auditor goes beyond mere compliance auditing and investigates opportunities for systemic QMS improvement. He or she assesses the client's QMS processes for compliance to ISO 9000 requirements, and leverages his or her own vast experience to make "observations" that the client could benefit from (however, the auditor is generally not permitted to offer consulting due to conflict of interest issues). An observation is a condition that could potentially become a problem, or has some limitation/deficiency that could be eliminated by due thought. In essence, with the help of observations, the auditor can point the organization to QMS-related issues that require closer examination. In order to make such insightful observations, it is necessary that the auditor have sound judgment and the ability to prioritize and focus on the vital few issues as opposed to the trivial many.

Typically, organizations adopt an informal approach to selecting their ISO 9000 registrar. Some of these include: interviewing a registrar referred by an acquaintance; inviting quotes from available registrars and selecting the lowest bid; selecting a registrar whom the organization met at an industry event for quality professionals, and so on. Such an approach to selecting an ISO 9000 registrar is not only haphazard and error-prone, it may be downright dangerous to the long-term goodness of the quality improvement efforts in the organization. Having a set of auditors who routinely perform surveillance audits and write up audit reports that go little beyond compliance auditing will only result in the independent third-party audits being regarded as a necessary evil to maintain the status quo. On the contrary, an auditor with a refreshing approach to auditing and committed to a true "partnership approach" with the client for the client's business improvement will earn the respect of the client's executive management team and be a great asset to the organization's internal quality department. This is especially important because once an organization has signed up as a client with a particular registrar, most of its future relationship with the registrar will be through the lead auditor assigned to it. Therefore, it is very important that before signing up with a registrar, an "auditor assessment" be performed as part of the registrar selection process. As an analogy, if one were in the market to purchase a new car, one of the influencing factors is, of course, the reputation and sales of the car company. However, one doesn't purchase a car by just talking to the salesman and studying glossy marketing brochures. The buyer takes a test drive because once the purchase decision is made, it is the car that the customer will interface with on a daily basis, not the car salesman! One has to know the product before one pays for it. In selecting a registrar, the product is the service offered by the registrar. Numerous publications attest to the fact that to go beyond mere compliance auditing requires special skills on behalf of the auditors.[1] Therefore, it is very desirable to be familiar with a registrar's auditing philosophy, operating style, quality of auditors, and registration experience of its current and past clients (obtained by requesting customer references that are discussed later). This chapter discusses the aforementioned issues and presents a systematic, and tried and tested process for performing registrar selection.

This chapter also provides a detailed insight into the overall ISO 9000 registration process, and the types of audits it entails. In addition, it includes valuable tips on how an organization can prepare itself for such audits, and what audit management activities need to be performed during the audits to ensure that the audits proceed smoothly.

SELECTING A REGISTRAR

Before discussing the ISO 9000 registration process, let's first study the registrar selection process in depth. Major steps in the registrar selection process are as follows:

1. Identify registrars to be mailed RFI questionnaire.

2. Prepare and send the RFI questionnaire to registrars.

3. Review RFI responses from registrars.

4. Interview short-listed registrars.

5. Make registrar selection decision.

The following subsections describe the aforementioned steps in detail.

Identify Registrars to be Mailed RFI Questionnaire

The initial step before mailing the RFI questionnaire is to determine which registrars are accredited to perform ISO 9000 registrations. An organization may contact the registrar to verify that the registrar is accredited by the respective national accreditation body to perform ISO 9000 registrations, or it may obtain this information directly from the registrar's Web site. For organizations in the United States, a list of registrars accredited to perform ISO 9000 registrations can be obtained from the RAB, by contacting them at 1-888-722-2440 or www.rabnet.com. Similarly, residents of other countries should contact their respective national accreditation body.

Once an organization has obtained the list of registrars, the next step is to determine how many registrars should be sent the RFI questionnaire. This is because there is effort required to review each RFI response, and an organization needs to decide how many responses it is willing to review. Some things to consider in making this determination are:

- Some of the registrars may not be in physical proximity, which can significantly add to the registration cost due to additional travel-related expenses (which have to be borne by the organization).

- All registrars under consideration must be accredited or should have a Memorandum of Understanding (MoU) with the respective national accreditation body of each country in which the organization has office locations that are planned to be registered.

Generally, it is advisable to consider no more than 10 registrars in the registrar selection process.

Prepare and Send the RFI Questionnaire to Registrars

The RFI questionnaire is prepared by the quality department and is a very important instrument to determine whether a registrar deserves to be considered any further in the registrar selection process. Therefore, all questions critical to making such an initial determination should be included in the questionnaire, along with adequate space for responses. A list of sample questions that may be included in the RFI is presented in Table 9.1; additional questions may be added as appropriate.

The RFI questionnaire should be accompanied with a cover letter and some organization literature to provide the registrar with adequate organizational information. The cover letter should contain information such as:

- A brief overview of the nature of the business of the organization, and a list of company locations that need to be registered

- A statement of scope of the QMS planned to be registered to ISO 9001:2000

- Head count of each department within the scope of the registration, along with total number of employees in the scope of the registration

- Any other information that the respondent may find useful when completing the RFI

The RFI questionnaire should clearly indicate the due date for completion and return of the questionnaire (minimally, a month should be provided), along with the complete contact information of the organization's management representative to whom the completed RFI may be mailed, e-mailed, or faxed.

Table 9.1 Sample RFI questionnaire.

Sample RFI Questionnaire

Return to: <Complete contact information of management representative>

Submission deadline: <date>

Instructions: Please complete the attached questionnaire. You may use supplementary sheets and you may include sales/marketing brochures with your response.

Respondent: <Complete contact information of the person completing this questionnaire>

1. *Experience:* Has your company previously registered companies in the software industry to ISO 9001:2000? If yes, please indicate approximately how many companies you have registered (you may include registrations to ISO 9000:1994 as well).

2. *Experience:* Have you previously registered companies of our size to ISO 9000?

3. *References:* Please provide company names, contact information of management representative, and a brief description of some of your clients in the same industry as ours.

4. *Reputation:* Does the software industry recognize you as an experienced registrar? Why?

5. *Recognition:* In what other countries is your registration formally recognized, that is, through a formal MoU agreement?

6. *Methodology:* Briefly describe your registration methodology. (Consider the following: documentation audit, preassessment audit, registration audit and its duration, allowed minor nonconformances, time provided to close major nonconformances and mechanism for follow-up, frequency and approach to surveillance audits, and approach to reregistration)

7. *Location:* Do you have an office in close proximity to our corporate head office and to our other locations that are to be registered (please refer to our organizational literature provided to you)? If yes, please provide their addresses.

8. *Auditor related:* What are your auditor selection criteria?

9. *Auditor related:* Can you provide qualifications and resume(s) of the proposed/candidate lead auditors for our organization? If yes, please enclose with the completed questionnaire.

10. *Auditor related:* In order to assist us in our registrar selection process, will you be able to arrange for the proposed lead auditor to meet in person with us?

11. *Cost:* Can you provide an initial estimate for the cost of this multisite registration?

12. *Cost:* What are your daily auditor and expense rates? (Consider the following: nonconformance follow-up visits)

13. Is there any other information you wish to provide?

Once the RFI questionnaire has been prepared, it may be sent to the registrars by regular mail, e-mail or fax.

Review RFI Responses from Registrars

Immediately after the RFI questionnaire is sent to the registrars, the method for assessing the registrar responses should be determined. This should be performed relatively quickly so that by the time the registrar responses start arriving, the method is already in place. In order to ensure that the final registrar rankings have the least subjectivity, it is preferable that the rankings be arrived at by using a method similar to the Wideband Delphi method.[2] This method should be applied by the quality department personnel and the management representative so that the final ranking is sound, based on consensus and not the sole opinion of only one person.[3] This method entails each of the reviewers reviewing the RFI responses and *independently* completing a registrar evaluation matrix (refer to Table 9.2). This includes recording information such as: the response date for each registrar, key observations from each RFI response, list of pros and cons (from studying the registrars' RFI responses and supporting documentation, if any), and relative rankings of the registrars. The reviewers then meet to discuss their assessment of the registrars, along with supporting rationale. During such discussions, consideration should be given to the relative importance of criteria used to compare one registrar against another. Based on these discussions, the reviewers may again rereview their assessment as they evolve a consensus on the final rankings.

Once the registrars have been ranked, the associated comments, and pros and cons from all reviewers' matrices should be consolidated into one final registrar evaluation matrix. The registrar selection process now proceeds to the next step: interviews of lead auditors from the short-listed registrars, preferably no more than three. It is preferable to limit the interviews to only a few registrars for the same reasons as described earlier—lead auditor interviews require time and effort to prepare for, perform, and analyze the interviews. Of course, the list of short-listed registrars may be extended to include lower-ranked registrars if after interviewing the short-listed registrars, the organization does not deem them worthy of selection.

Interview Short-Listed Registrars

Once registrars have been short-listed, the management representative and the quality department should start preparing for the lead auditor interviews. It is preferable to hold a face-to-face lead auditor interview, but an interview by teleconference or videoconference is also acceptable. Generally, registrars

Table 9.2 Informal tracking and review of registrar responses (partial table only).

ISO 9000 Registrar Selection: Registrar Evaluation Matrix

RFI mailed on: July 15, 2003
Completed RFI due by: August 15, 2003

#	Registrar	Final Response Received	Comments on RFI response process	Pros	Cons	Rank
1	ABC Company	Aug. 8, 2003	• Registrar lost RFI and requested it be resent • Lost RFI a second time and again requested it be resent!	• 33,000 ISO 9000 certifications to date • Impressive client list • Only registrar who seems to offer a fixed, all-inclusive cost for registration • Close to most of our office locations	• Sloppy work ethic: they lost our RFI twice! • Auditor resumes were not provided in spite of us asking for them • Bad recommendation from a key customer who indicated this registrar is known to be very rigid, inflexible	5
2	XYZ Company	July 24, 2003	• Quick and comprehensive response	• 2000 ISO 9000 certifications to date • Impressive client list • Good response package • Close to all our office locations • One of the rare auditors to have full-time employees as auditors • Repeatedly encouraged us to speak with any reference • Excellent independent reference from two key customers	• Same auditors might not be maintained for surveillance audits, therefore, there is risk of inconsistency	1
3	⋮					

are more than willing to arrange for an interview with the proposed lead auditor, but sometimes the registrar may not be able to say which lead auditor would ultimately be assigned the customer account. In that case, it is still desirable to request an interview with a lead auditor of the registrar, so as to gauge the registrar's auditing philosophy. Bear in mind that most registrars try their best to ensure consistency across their auditors; therefore, interviewing one lead auditor gives a good idea of the registrar's auditing philosophy and approach.

The purpose of the lead auditor interview is to allow the organization an opportunity to gauge the proposed lead auditor for traits such as:

- Lead auditor's auditing style. Is the lead auditor primarily interested in records-based auditing to solely identify infractions against the ISO 9001:2000 standard, or is the lead auditor interested in the *big picture* and in partnering with the organization to bring about real quality improvement?

- Does the lead auditor have preconceived notions regarding how an organization should comply with a stated requirement?

- Is the lead auditor knowledgeable in the organization's specific industry domain?

It is preferable not to have more than two interviewers; these interviewers should have also previously reviewed the registrar's RFI response. Both interviewers should maintain personal notes from the meeting for post-meeting analysis. Some of the questions that may be asked during the interview are:

1. What is the lead auditor's prior experience in performing ISO 9001:2000 audits of companies in the software industry, and specifically in your area of business?

2. How many companies in the software industry has the lead auditor himself (or herself) registered in a lead auditor role?

3. Which companies is the lead auditor currently a lead auditor for? For the purpose of a reference check, is the lead auditor willing to provide you with the contact information of some of the customers' management representatives?

4. What are the lead auditor's thoughts and interpretation regarding applicability to the software industry of:

   - Measurement-related requirements in ISO 9001:2000?

   - Calibration-related requirements in ISO 9001:2000?

5. How long has the lead auditor been associated with the registrar?

6. Are all auditors full-time employees of the registrar?

7. If you select the registrar, will a customer manager be assigned to your account, or will you have to directly coordinate the audits with the lead auditor (which may be difficult due to frequent travel of the lead auditor)?

Additional things to consider during the interview (unique to each registrar):

1. Are any clarifications needed on the registrar's RFI response?

2. Investigate areas of registrar's weakness that were identified from the review of the registrar's RFI response.

3. Confirm the registrar's strengths that were identified from the review of the registrar's RFI response.

Also, at this stage, for each of the short-listed registrars, a request for quotation (RFQ) should be sent out by the procurement department to obtain the detailed breakdown of all costs related to the registration audit and three-year surveillance audit period. This is because registration-related costs are typically an important consideration for the final selection decision.

Make Registrar Selection Decision

Based on the information gathered from the review of the registrars' RFI responses, interviews of the lead auditors, and review of registrar responses to the RFQ, the appropriate personnel should have an open discussion to compare their observations regarding relative strengths and weaknesses of the various registrars. Recommendation for selection of a registrar should be arrived at by consensus and the recommendation should be presented at the QMS management review for consideration and approval by senior management. Once final approval has been obtained from senior management, signoff on the three-year contractual agreement and nondisclosure agreement[4] can be initiated.

ISO 9000 REGISTRATION PROCESS

The ISO 9000 registration process is more or less the same across all registrars, barring minor differences that are not significant to this discussion. This process can be divided into three phases:

- Preassessment audit(s)

- Registration audit

- Surveillance audits

Registration and surveillance audits are required to achieve and maintain ISO 9000 registration, while preassessment audits are optional.

The registration and surveillance audits are scheduled by the organization's management representative in consultation with the registrar. The management representative serves as the interface between the organization and its registrar. He or she is therefore responsible for providing information to and requesting information from the registrar, and for disseminating pertinent information, such as the audit plan, to the organization's employees.

Preassessment Audit

A preassessment audit, as the name suggests, is performed prior to the registration audit and is a preliminary audit to assess compliance to ISO 9001:2000, and to the organization's QMS documentation. The preassessment audit is generally performed about two or three months prior to the registration audit. This provides the organization adequate time to implement requested corrective and preventive actions in time for the registration audit. In essence, a preassessment audit is equivalent to a mock registration audit, although the scope of the preassessment audit is generally much smaller than the registration audit. The scope of the preassessment audit is determined by the organization being audited. Therefore, while one organization may have 10 percent of its QMS preassessed, another may have 25 percent of its QMS preassessed. Generally, organizations limit their preassessment to about 10–15 percent of the QMS.

The preassessment audit does not necessarily have to be performed by the organization's registrar; it may also be performed by a third-party consultant, or internally by the organization's employees who are qualified as quality auditors. However, for reasons described later, it is always desirable that the preassessment audit, if performed, be performed by the organization's ISO 9000 registrar.

Some registrars offer two types of preassessment, which for a lack of commonly accepted names, will be referred to as "a preassessment that does not count" (also called a "throwaway preassessment") and "a preassessment that counts." A throwaway preassessment is one where an organization has complete freedom in deciding what and how many parts of the QMS it would like preassessed. Such a preassessment is solely to enable an organization to assess its preparedness for the registration audit. An organization is neither credited for complying nor penalized for identified nonconformances. Simply put, such a preassessment audit does not count toward the registration audit.

On the other hand, a preassessment that counts enables an organization to have limited parts of its QMS preassessed for registration credit. What this means is that those elements of the QMS that are preassessed without any noted audit findings can be regarded as having been successfully ISO 9000 registered (although without the issuance of a formal registration certificate), provided such a preassessment was performed within six months prior to the registration audit. For elements that are preassessed with audit findings, the organization has a certain amount of time, typically until the registration audit, to implement corrective and preventive actions.

Having discussed the different types of preassessment audits, let's examine some of the benefits associated with a preassessment audit:

1. First and foremost, it enables the organization to assess its overall readiness for the registration audit. Typically, a successful preassessment provides a high degree of assurance that the organization is ready for the registration audit. However, this is not always true because the elements of the QMS that are preassessed are determined by the organization, while the elements that will be covered during the registration audit are not. Therefore, during the registration audit, the organization may be determined to be deficient in certain QMS elements that were not covered in the preassessment audit. In the worst-case scenario, if the organization determines that it has serious deficiencies in numerous areas, then, in consultation with its registrar, it may choose to delay its planned registration audit date.

2. A preassessment audit helps in performing effective risk mitigation in areas where the organization fears it may not be fully compliant with applicable requirements. For example, if the organization's internal quality audits have revealed that the organization has historically been weak in certain elements of the QMS, and identified corrective and preventive actions have been taken, then it would be advisable to have these elements preassessed. This will help the organization assess if these areas are mature enough to withstand the rigors of a full-blown ISO 9000 audit and that they do not pose undue risk to jeopardize the organization's overall ISO 9000 registration plans. If the organization is found to have only a limited deficiency in the preassessed elements, then it can implement needed corrective and preventive actions in preparation for the registration audit. However, if it has serious deficiencies, then as stated earlier, it may choose to delay its registration plans.

It is important to note that this is one of the reasons why it is advantageous to have the preassessment performed by the organization's registrar because it provides the assurance to the organization that its areas of concern have been examined by the same registrar that would perform the actual registration audit (although not necessarily the same auditors). It therefore eliminates the risk of having areas of concern be deemed adequate by a third-party consultant, yet be deemed inadequate by the organization's registrar at the time of the registration audit. Such an unfortunate situation would defeat one of the objectives of having the preassessment audit itself.

3. If the organization engages its registrar to perform the preassessment, it provides an excellent opportunity to experience a mock registration audit. That is, it enables the organization to familiarize itself with the auditing style of its lead auditor (representing the registrar). It also enables the auditor(s) to get to know the client and become familiar with the organization's products and services.

Having discussed the benefits of preassessment audits, it is easy to predict the general strategy an organization should adopt as it schedules parts of its QMS for a preassessment audit. In order to maximize the utility of the preassessment audit(s), it is beneficial to schedule the areas of most concern for the preassessment audit(s). This enables the organization to obtain the registrar's independent assessment of the areas deemed to be of concern. While the organization's internal quality auditors should be able to make such a determination if they are adequately qualified, there may be situations where they face internal resistance or difference in opinion regarding how to effectively comply with a stated ISO 9001:2000 requirement. After all, most internal quality auditors, at some time or other have heard, "Our process fully complies with the applicable ISO 9001:2000 requirements. I don't see how any external ISO 9000 auditor could have a problem with this!" or "In my previous company, we were never asked to do what you are asking, yet we were ISO 9000 registered!" Presenting such contentious areas in front of the registrar during the preassessment audit(s) helps obtain an independent assessment of the adequacy of the implementation, and if the internal quality personnel are indeed right, confirmation of their position by the external auditor can decide the issue in their favor. Keep in mind that the contrary is also sometimes true, wherein the organization may be overzealous in interpreting a particular requirement and go beyond what any external auditor would reasonably expect!

If the organization is undergoing a preassessment that counts, then in order to demonstrate progress to its customers toward its ISO 9001:2000 registration goal, the organization may decide to have certain relatively solid QMS elements preassessed (that is, safe bets). The rationale being that having some QMS elements successfully registered to ISO 9000, albeit unofficially, will enable the organization to informally demonstrate to its customers the independent validation of certain parts of its QMS. The organization may also choose to do so for other reasons, such as leveraging the small victory as a confidence booster ahead of the registration audit.

All the audit findings from the preassessment audit(s) are documented in a formal audit report by the lead auditor. As in the registration audit report, each audit finding will reference the clause or subclause of the ISO 9001:2000 standard against which it is noted as a nonconformance. (Refer to corrective action request form in appendix B.) As in the case of internal quality audits, the audit report should be provided to management personnel by the management representative. The management representative should then coordinate the corrective and/or preventive action planning and timely implementation with the respective departments.

Registration Audit

During the registration audit, the external auditors, led by the lead auditor, examine whether quality activities are being performed in accordance with ISO 9001:2000 requirements and the organization's internal requirements (as stated in its QMS documentation). If the organization successfully passes the registration audit, the lead auditor will recommend ISO 9000 registration for the organization to the registrar. If nonconformances are found, then the major nonconformances must be resolved before registration can proceed. Details on how the lead auditor determines whether or not to recommend the organization for registration are discussed later in this chapter. Guidance on how to prepare for the registration audit and subsequent surveillance audits is provided later in this chapter.

Overall, the registration audit process is very similar to the internal audit process described in chapter 8. However, there are some differences associated with the registration audit process; therefore, it is desirable to discuss it separately.

Registration Audit Plan

Once the organization has selected an ISO 9000 registrar, the first activity that the registrar will initiate is the formulation of the audit plan. The audit plan is a two-dimensional matrix that serves as the road map to show how the organization's QMS is audited over the three-year registration period. The audit plan is a living document as explained later in this section. Note that not all processes and departments need to be audited as part of the registration audit. The lead auditor will establish the audit plan in accordance with the guidance provided by the respective national registrar accreditation body, such as the RAB.

Due to the process-oriented nature of ISO 9001:2000, the audit plan matrix may be prepared in a process-oriented fashion, wherein the organization's key QMS processes and/or procedures are listed along one axis, and all organizational departments in scope of the ISO 9001:2000 registration are listed along the other axis. Alternatively, the audit plan may list all ISO 9001:2000 clauses along one axis, and organizational departments along the other. Table 9.3 shows an example of an audit plan matrix for an organization that is assumed to have undergone a preassessment audit but not the registration surveillance audits. Note that this example is provided only to illustrate what an audit plan may look like; the example is not necessarily complete and correct in terms of depicting applicability of ISO 9001:2000 requirements to relevant organizational departments.

The audit plan is prepared incrementally, that is, initially the auditor will simply list along the x and y axes what areas need to be audited without identifying when they will be audited. Then, a few days prior to an audit, the lead auditor typically will provide an updated audit plan to the management representative identifying the areas that will be audited in the upcoming audit, along with an audit schedule communicating the time and duration of the audits. The number of person-days that the lead auditor allocates for an audit, which in turn impacts the number of additional auditors he or she may bring, is dependent upon the number of employees to be audited and dictated by the guidelines established by the registrar accreditation body.

Once an audit is completed, the lead auditor will typically revise the audit plan to indicate what departments were audited in the latest audit. The audit plan is a living document that is continually updated before and after the various audits during an organization's three-year registration period.

Documentation Audit

The necessary first step in the registration audit is an audit of the organization's quality manual and QMS documentation against applicable ISO 9001:2000 requirements. The purpose of this exercise is to assess whether all applicable requirements of the standard have been adequately addressed in the organization's QMS. Once the documentation audit is complete, and noted audit findings have been addressed by the organization, audit interviews are initiated.

Table 9.3 QMS process/procedure-oriented sample audit plan.

Process	Senior Mgmt.	Management Representative	Documentation Management	Contracts	Project Mgmt.	Design & Development	Procurement	System Test	Customer Service	Human Resources
Quality system documentation		X								
Continuous improvement processes		X								
Management commitment and management review	X	X								
Customer focus	X	X								X	
Product and process measurement		X								
Internal audits		X								
Contract review process				P						
Project planning, tracking and oversight					X					
Product requirements definition						X				
Requirements analysis and product design						X				
Subcontractor management		P					P			
Procurement							X			

Continued

Continued

Department / Process	Senior Mgmt.	Management Representative	Documentation Management	Contracts	Project Mgmt.	Design & Development	Procurement	System Test	Customer Service	Human Resources
Product development						X				
Change control						P				
Product test								X		
Control of product						X				
Documentation and record control			X							
Customer calls management									X	
Employee competence and training										X

Legend:

P: Preassessment audit

R: Registration audit (not yet used)

S1: Surveillance audit 1 (not yet used)

S2: Surveillance audit 2 (not yet used)

S3: Surveillance audit 3 (not yet used)

S4: Surveillance audit 4 (not yet used)

S5: Surveillance audit 5 (not yet used)

X: Not yet audited

Opening Meeting

The registration audit begins with an opening meeting, similar to the one described in chapter 8. Generally, invitees to the opening meeting are limited to management personnel from the areas being audited.

Conducting of the Audit

The external auditors use the same auditing techniques as described in chapter 8, namely, audit interviews, observation of activities, and examination of evidence. The auditors typically work in parallel and concurrently audit different departments and personnel. After completion of the audits, the auditors collectively meet with the lead auditor to share and discuss their audit findings. After considering the audit team's input, the lead auditor makes all final decisions regarding the validity and severity of the noted audit finding(s). As in the internal quality audits, during the registration audit interviews, the auditor will clearly indicate to the auditee(s) the nature of any possible audit findings (subject to review with the lead auditor). In other words, upon completion of each audit, all auditees would be aware of noted deficiencies, and there should be no surprises in the closing meeting and audit report that follow later.

A unique feature of the registration audit is the use of *guides* by the organization to escort the auditors and attend the audit interviews. Quality department personnel should serve as guides. To avoid a situation where the auditors feel overwhelmed by the guides, no more than one guide should be present at an audit interview. Guides should be cognizant of the fact that they are intended to be *silent* attendees during the audits and they should never answer the question posed to the auditee, or help the auditee in answering the questions.

Primary responsibilities of a guide are as follows (some additional responsibilities are provided later in this chapter):

• Request rephrasing or clarification of the question posed if the guide perceives that the auditee is unable to comprehend the question. With the auditor's permission, the guide may translate the question in the context of the auditee's activities and applicable QMS documents.

• Monitor the auditor's interpretation of the ISO 9001:2000 requirements in the context of the organization's business. Request a clarification of expectations if the guide disagrees with the auditor's interpretation, and inform the auditor of the organization's interpretation of the requirement. Sometimes, the auditor may be willing to accommodate the organizational interpretation of the requirement (provided that it is a reasonable interpretation that is consistent with the intent of the requirement). However, if the auditor disagrees, the guides should never initiate an argument on the issue and must let the audit interview proceed by respecting the auditor's view and decision. In the rare instance that an organization has serious differences with the auditor's interpretation of a requirement, mechanisms typically exist that allow the organization to escalate the issue above the lead auditor to the respective registration manager representing the registrar. (Contact the registrar for more details.) That said, such a scenario is very unlikely because all auditors are required to undergo standardized training to foster a consistent interpretation and understanding of ISO 9001:2000 requirements. Further, this understanding is enhanced and solidified by virtue of performing a vast number of ISO 9000 registration and surveillance audits of various organizations.

• Identify opportunities for internal quality improvement from the audit interviews.

Upon completion of the audit interviews for each audit day, the audit team typically meets with the management personnel from the areas audited, or minimally with the management representative, to review the day's audit findings. If possible, noted audit findings may be corrected prior to the completion of the audit. As a matter of standard auditing practice, auditors include such audit findings in the final audit report (with the explanation that they are already closed).

Closing Meeting

Upon completion of the registration audit, the lead auditor holds a closing meeting with the management personnel from the areas audited to apprise them of the audit findings and the preliminary registration decision. If there are no major or minor audit findings, then the lead auditor will immediately recommend ISO 9000 registration for the organization to the registrar's office.

Major or minor findings are handled in the following fashion: In case of minor audit findings, the lead auditor will request a corrective action plan from the organization within a specific time frame. The lead auditor will review the corrective action plan for acceptability, and once deemed acceptable, will recommend ISO 9000 registration for the organization. In other words, it is permissible to implement corrective actions for minor findings after the ISO 9000 registration has been awarded, but no later than the next surveillance audit. On the other hand, in the case of major audit findings, the lead auditor will request a corrective action plan *and implementation* within a specific time frame, typically 90 days, before registration can be recommended. The organization may negotiate additional time with the registrar, within the time frame allowed by the respective accreditation body. Generally, it is required that all major audit findings be resolved within six months of the registration audit, if registration is to proceed; otherwise, a new registration audit would be required. The management representative should work with the appropriate management personnel for corrective action planning and implementation as per the time frame agreed to with the registrar. Once required actions have been implemented, the lead auditor will verify the implemented actions for adequacy and effectiveness before recommending ISO 9000 registration for the organization.

☞ In all cases, it is important to realize a point that is emphasized by all registrars—that the registration audit should never be viewed as a pass or fail verdict, because it isn't. In most cases, the occurrence of one or more major audit findings merely *delays* an organization's recommendation for registration, until such time that the required corrective action has been implemented and verified.

Audit Report

Within two to four weeks of the audit closing meeting, irrespective of the outcome of the audit, the lead auditor provides a formal audit report to the management representative, including a registration decision. The management representative should share the audit report with the management personnel and employees (if appropriate) of the areas audited.

Registration Decision

Once the registrar approves ISO 9000 registration for the organization, it is time for some well-deserved celebration! The quality department should ensure that a celebration event, such as an all-hands pizza lunch and quality giveaway, is planned. This event may be planned immediately upon being notified about the lead auditor's decision to recommend registration, or it may be planned after the registration is formally obtained. Typically, if the organization has been recommended for registration, the registration certificate will arrive in the mail about four to six weeks after the registration audit. The registrar will inquire about the number of copies of the certificate the organization requires for posting at its facilities.

The certificate will clearly state the scope of the registration and what sites are included in the registration. The organization must ensure not to represent its registration to imply inclusion of sites and/or activities that were not actually included in the registration. An organization should *never* in any way imply registration of a product to ISO 9000, because it is the organization itself that is registered to ISO 9000, not its products.

Publicizing the Registration

In order to enable an organization to publicize its registration, most registrars provide paid and unpaid marketing support and material. Unpaid marketing support typically includes listing the organization in the directory of all organizations registered to ISO 9000 by the registrar; a directory that is categorized by industry segment and distributed worldwide to all the registrar's customers. Depending on the international reputation and clientele of the registrar, inclusion in such a directory can serve as a valuable marketing tool for new business opportunities. Paid marketing support includes providing ISO 9000 flags, banners, and posters for display in the organization's facilities, and electronic graphics files for display of the ISO 9000 registered logo on the organization's Web site. Again, it is not permissible that the ISO 9000 registered logo be included on product packaging to imply registration of the product, but it is permissible to include the ISO 9000 registered logo on sales and marketing brochures, letterheads, and business cards.

Surveillance Audits

Once an organization is successful in obtaining ISO 9000 registration for the three-year period, it must continue to demonstrate adherence to the requirements contained in the standard and in its own QMS documentation. This requires that the registrar periodically audit the organization to verify continued compliance. These mandatory periodic audits are called surveillance audits. Each surveillance audit entails an assessment of only part of the QMS.

Surveillance audits are generally performed at six-month intervals and are scheduled jointly by the lead auditor and the management representative. An organization may also choose to have surveillance audits less frequently, but at no more than 12-month intervals. In that case, the duration of each surveillance audit will be longer than what it would be if surveillance audits were performed on six-month intervals. Most organizations choose to schedule surveillance audits at six-month intervals. This provides a reasonably frequent opportunity for timely identification of deficiencies that may have crept into the QMS, as opposed to audits that are much farther apart.

As stated earlier, a few days prior to the surveillance audit, the lead auditor will provide a detailed plan of areas to be audited. Additionally, the auditor(s) will follow up on audit findings from the previous audit (registration or surveillance audit, as applicable). Certain key clauses of ISO 9001:2000 will be audited at *each* surveillance audit. These typically are: management reviews, internal audits, corrective actions, preventive actions, handling of customer complaints, control of documents, impact of organizational changes on the QMS, and proper use of ISO 9001:2000 registration certificates.[5]

As with the registration audit, the registrar will provide an audit report for each surveillance audit. Major and minor audit findings are handled in the same fashion as for the registration audit. Occurrence of major audit findings in surveillance audits does not typically lead to revocation of an organization's ISO 9000 registration unless there has been a continued systemic breakdown of the QMS and clearly perceptible waning in organizational commitment to quality and ISO 9000. Therefore, there are only rare instances of organizations losing their ISO 9000 registration.

Upon completion of the three-year registration period, the process repeats itself—a reregistration audit, followed by surveillance audits over another three-year registration period.

PREPARATION TIPS FOR THE REGISTRATION AUDIT

As the date of the registration audit approaches, final preparations should be initiated—both for the purpose of giving a final push to the entire organization toward the coveted goal, as well as for ensuring that all the logistics pertaining to the actual registration audit are in place. Further, once the registration audit is underway, the management representative should ensure that steps are taken to:

- Minimize surprises during the audit.
- Control parts of the audit that the auditor is willing to let you control.
- Minimize deviations from the agreed audit plan.
- In the event of genuine difference of opinion with the auditor, share your opinion with the auditor in an unobtrusive way.

The following two subsections elaborate on these issues. These tips are applicable to the preparation and management of surveillance audits as well.

Audit Preparation

In essence, audit preparations really begin the day an organization decides to pursue an ISO 9001:2000 registration. However, they gradually ramp up and reach a crescendo closer to the registration audit date. This section describes final preparations before the audit. These final preparations pertain to employee preparation and planning for audit logistics.

Employee Preparation

1. In the weeks and days leading up to the registration audit, gradually change the theme in the posters and bulletin boards to audit preparation. For example, the posters should increasingly emphasize key elements of the organization's QMS, and auditee preparation for the audit interviews. Some sample posters are shown in Figures 9.1.a and 9.1.b.

2. Approximately two weeks before the registration audit date, a heads-up e-mail or memo should be sent to all employees in the scope of the registration. The purpose of this communication is to provide information on dos and don'ts associated with the audit, this includes: interviewing tips, advice on work space preparation, and information regarding some of the standard audit questions (see sidebar). The message should be brief yet complete. A succinct message is more likely to be read and understood by the targeted audience as opposed to a long-winded message that may be

---

WORK SPACE PREPARATION TIPS FOR EMPLOYEES:

- Make sure your work space is clean. Be aware that the auditor may come to your work space to inspect objective evidence.

- Ensure that all QMS documents that pertain to your area of work are available and approved (as appropriate). This entails ensuring that the version of any controlled document you are using or referencing in your document is the most current and approved version. All hard-copy obsolete documents must be discarded or marked "obsolete."

Continued

Continued

INTERVIEW PREPARATION TIPS FOR EMPLOYEES:

- Treat the auditor with respect and be courteous. Turn off cell phones and pagers during the audit interview.

- For the audit interview, only bring a personal notebook and material that the auditor has specifically requested.

- During the audit interview, only answer the question asked. Be succinct but don't hide anything. Stop when you feel that you have answered the question. Do *not* fill gaps of silence.

- When responding to a question, keep in mind that the auditor may ask to see objective evidence to confirm what you say.

- Do *not* answer questions that are not in your area of responsibility. Defer them to the appropriate personnel.

- You may ask the auditor to restate or rephrase a question if you do not understand it.

- Do *not* request the quality department guide for help to respond to the auditor's questions.

- During the interview, be positive at all times. Do *not* voluntarily present problems faced with other departments (or office locations). However, you should discuss these internally with the quality department so that timely corrective or preventive action can be taken.

- Finally, be calm and relax during the audit! Remember, the auditor is there to perform a process assessment and not personnel assessment!

TYPICAL AUDIT QUESTIONS:

Provide the employees with typical audit questions[6] for their respective areas. If certain employees are in a state of panic and ill at ease with the imminent audit, consider performing mock audit interviews with them to help prepare them and ease them into the external audit process. Note that such a situation may arise with employees who have never previously been audited.

You
could be an auditee at the
upcoming registration audit!!
Are you ***prepared*???**

- Some typical auditor questions:
  - Can you show an organization chart of your department?
  - What are your responsibilities?
  - What is your company's quality policy?
  - Can you show the procedures that you are using for your activities?
  - Please walk me through the process described in your procedure.
  - What quality records are generated as a result of implementing this process?

Figure 9.1.a   Sample quality poster.

QMS Quick Facts

- Our Quality Policy "To deliver excellent quality products and services to our customers by continuous process improvement."
- Our Quality Management Representative: David Avis
- Our QMS has a four-tier structure:
  - Tier 1: Quality manual
  - Tier 2: Quality procedures
  - Tier 3: Work instructions, forms, and templates
  - Tier 4: Quality records

Figure 9.1.b   Sample quality poster.

disregarded. Or even worse, the audience might be unable to retain the advice and may feel overwhelmed with too much information!

3. Provide employees information about the "five Ws" (what, why, when, where, who) regarding the upcoming audit, and advise them on how they may obtain additional information in case they have any questions.

- "What" pertains to describing the scope of the audit (that is, general areas that are planned to be audited)

- "Why" pertains to reason(s) for conducting the audit, for example, for ISO 9000 registration purpose (registration audit), or for the maintenance of ISO 9000 registration (surveillance audit)

- "When" pertains to the date(s) when the audit will be performed

- "Where" pertains to the office location(s) where the audit will be performed

- "Who" pertains to which departments will be audited

4. Inform employees about the purpose of internal quality guides, and inform them who will be the guides for the upcoming audit. This way employees will expect some quality department personnel during the audit interviews. Knowing for what purpose they are there, employees will be comfortable in their presence.

5. Again, all employees should be advised only to answer questions in their area of responsibility, and defer questions pertaining to another area to the responsible person for the other area. To enable them to do this, all employees should be provided a list of all areas to be audited along with a responsible contact person for each. Alternatively, auditees may defer the question to the management representative if they do not know who the responsible person for the other area is. The internal quality guide may also provide this information, if during the audit interview the auditee is unable to identify who to defer the question to. Minimally, it is expected from the auditee that he or she knows how to find out who the responsible person for the other area is. Therefore, if questioned, it is expected that at least the auditee should state that he or she could obtain this information from his or her manager.

Audit Logistics

The following list provides examples of preparation required for audit logistics:

1. A dedicated meeting room should be reserved for the audit team to serve as their base of operations. In case the audit interviews are to take place in a meeting room and there will be multiple auditors auditing in parallel, then more meeting rooms will need to be reserved.

2. In cases where the QMS has been implemented online, if appropriate, set up a computer in the meeting room to facilitate direct access to the QMS.

3. Approximately two weeks before the audit, ask the auditor who should be invited to the opening and closing meetings. Immediately inform the required attendees to ensure that they plan their work schedule accordingly.

4. In many cases, the lead auditor permits the organization to pick the auditees for the audit interviews. Lead auditors often provide this liberty to the organizations because they know that, eventually, as part of the various surveillance audits, the organization will have to cycle other employees through the external audits. Therefore, the likelihood of the organization indulging in trickery and recycling the same auditees through the audit process is remote because it can easily be noticed by the auditors.

Unless the lead auditor indicates otherwise, it may be assumed that the organization has the liberty to select the auditees. For example, say the auditor says he or she wants to audit test personnel. If the auditor is not more specific, you may present the test manager only, or two senior test engineers, or whatever suits you best. To be prepared for such a situation, a list of standby auditees should be prepared once the audit plan has been provided by the lead auditor. The list of standby auditees should be reviewed and approved by the respective department management, and identified auditees should be asked to confirm their availability for the audit. At the same time, all management personnel should be told that the auditor(s) will have unrestricted access to the audit areas and may request to speak with any employee in the audited areas; therefore, all employees should be prepared to be audited. Management personnel are responsible for ensuring that their personnel are adequately prepared.

Factors that should be considered when preparing the list of standby auditees are:

- Employee's awareness of dos and don'ts when being interviewed by external auditors.

- Whether the employee is in the scope of the activities and projects to be audited.

- It is highly desirable that the employee already have been audited in at least one internal quality audit.

- Employee's familiarity with the QMS documents being audited; for this reason, selecting a very new employee would be inappropriate.

- Communication skills of the employee.

- Ensure that the complete set of standby auditees is such that together they provide the external auditor with the most complete picture of the area being audited (that is, include management personnel as well as practitioners).

Next, it is recommended that the quality department conduct mock audit interviews with the standby auditees. This includes audit of projects and documentation that the quality department feels the external auditor(s) will likely audit. Again, it should be emphasized to the management personnel that the external auditor(s) may choose to speak with any employee—they are not restricted to standby auditees only. However, it is desirable to pay some special attention to the standby auditees.

5. Prepare a welcome sign with the registrar's and lead auditor's names for display in the reception area.

6. Provide a tour of the facilities to the auditors so they feel comfortable in their new environment.

7. Inform the auditors of any organizational policies applicable to visitors, for example, ESD protective gear, lab coat policy, and so on.

8. In the case of product development audits, at the time of the audit interviews, the auditor may allow the organization to choose the project(s) to be audited. Therefore, prepare for this situation by deciding in advance with the relevant department managers which project(s) to short-list for the audit. Bear in mind that, typically, auditors prefer to audit the *same* project across various departments. This enables them to perform forward (and backward) traceability within a specific project as it progresses through various stages in different departments. This in turn enables them to identify process breakdowns and disconnects between different functional areas. Keeping this in mind, the projects recommended for the audit should preferably span the entire SPDP.

9. If there are major audit findings outstanding from internal quality audits, then, when feasible, ensure that they are satisfactorily implemented and closed before the external audit. Be aware that the auditors may choose to perform a random sampling of the implemented actions to verify the adequacy of follow-up performed by the internal quality auditors. Also, ensure that there are no overdue corrective and/or preventive actions, and if there are, the quality department should have an adequate explanation to provide to the external auditors (if asked).

Audit Management

In addition to preparations that need to be made as the registration audit approaches, the management representative should also ensure that control mechanisms are established to manage the audit once the audit interviews get under way. Some of the steps that should be taken to ensure the smooth conduct of the audit are:

1. Reemphasize auditing dos and don'ts to the auditees just prior to the audit interviews.

2. If the auditor is conducting audit interviews in a meeting room, then immediately before an interview, the guide should ask the auditor what hard-copy documentation needs to be brought to the audit room. This enables the quality department to ensure only documentation relevant to the audit interview is brought by the auditees. In case the auditor is conducting audit interviews in the work areas, advise the auditees in advance to only present to the auditor what the auditor specifically asks for.

3. Sometimes during the registration audit, as the auditors begin to develop an improved understanding of the organization's operations after speaking with various employees, they may request to audit areas that they had not originally included in their audit plan—mostly due to oversight, lack of sufficient information, or an incorrect assumption. Generally speaking, the management representative should request the lead auditor to stick to the audit plan. This is because unplanned audits may cause interruption in operations and may be difficult to support because the affected employees might be unavailable or busy with other tasks (since they were not notified in advance to be available for the audit). Generally, most lead auditors, being eager to provide good customer service, will postpone requests for such unplanned audits to a subsequent surveillance audit, unless the omission significantly impacts the current audit. In the latter case, the organization should do its best to accommodate the lead auditor's revised audit plans, but such cases of change in audit plans should be rare exceptions.

4. During some audits, the auditor might *not* ask to visit employee work areas and instead may prefer that identified objective evidence be brought to the interview room. In such a case, you need not ask the auditor if he or she wants to visit employee work areas to examine objective evidence. It is the auditor's responsibility to seek objective evidence that confirms or contradicts what is stated in the audit interviews; the auditees should present all requested information in an open and truthful manner. The auditees need not voluntarily draw the auditor's attention to known cases of noncompliance with an ISO 9001:2000 requirement(s) or internal QMS documentation(s); however, they must work with the quality department to ensure appropriate and timely internal corrective and/or preventive action to address the known issues.

5. When the auditor indicates intent to report an audit finding, the auditee(s) and guide should ensure that they understand exactly what the deficiency is, and what ISO 9001:2000 requirement or internal QMS requirement has been violated. In the event of genuine difference of opinion

with the auditor regarding the proposed audit finding, they should share their opinion with the auditor in an unobtrusive way. If it is a valid issue, the auditor may rescind the audit finding, may downgrade it, or may ask for additional evidence to substantiate the auditee's claim. At all times, the final authority to decide if indeed an audit finding is warranted rests with the auditor and not the auditee. Therefore, the auditee should never become obnoxious, overly defensive, or begin arguing with the auditor, as that would be unprofessional and against the spirit of quality audits.

6. Sometimes when the auditor identifies a violation of an ISO 9001:2000 requirement or an internal QMS document and is immediately informed by the quality department that the same audit finding was found in an internal quality audit, then the auditor may downgrade the severity of the audit finding if an approved corrective or preventive action plan already exists. Therefore, the guide should assess each proposed audit finding to determine if it has been reported from an internal audit, in which case the auditor should be informed. That said, there are cases when due to the nature of the proposed audit finding, the auditor may decide against downgrading the severity of the proposed audit finding, in which case the quality department should not argue and impede the auditor.

7. The guide should keep track of all material that the auditor requests during the audit interviews. The requested material should be provided to the auditor in the time frame requested. In case the auditor wishes to retain some material, the guide should ensure that necessary permissions have been obtained to allow external release of the proprietary information.

8. Finally, during the audit interview perhaps one of the most challenging tasks is for the auditees and quality guides to pay very close attention to what the auditor says and *use* that information to try to stay one step ahead of the auditor. This entails keeping track of what objective evidence the auditor indicates he or she needs to examine (or may need to examine), observing the auditor's auditing style, and predicting where the auditor's questioning may lead next. The quality guides may use this information to advise subsequent auditees about the auditor's auditing style, which will thus put them more at ease during the audit interviews. Similarly, by trying to stay one step of ahead of the auditor, once the audit interview heads down a certain path, the auditee can mentally prepare for the next thing the auditor may ask. This works best when the auditor is interviewing more than one auditee simultaneously. Because only one auditee would respond to the auditor at a given time, it enables the other auditees to think ahead and prepare. For example, the auditee may think of examples or instances to substantiate his response for the question that he expects the auditor to

ask next. Alternatively, once one auditee begins describing a particular document or activity to the auditor, the other auditee can *think ahead* about what might be a good example to present in case the auditor asks for one.

The importance of staying ahead of the auditor plays an important role in the success of an organization during the audit. It enables the auditees to stay relaxed and confident during the audit. Such *real-time preparation* for the audit interview is analogous to driving to a location for the first time versus driving there a second time. Having familiarized himself (or herself) with the route and the location once already (in this case, by thinking about the response to an anticipated question), the driver is more comfortable and self-assured driving there a second time (when the auditor actually asks the question that the auditee had anticipated)!

ENDNOTES

1. Arter, D., "Beyond Compliance: An Examination of Compliance and Management Auditing," *Quality Progress* (June 2000).
2. Boehm, B., *Software Engineering Economics* (Englewood Cliffs, NJ: Prentice Hall, 1982).
3. It is acknowledged that it may not be possible to use this mechanism in very small organizations.
4. The nondisclosure agreement is a legally binding agreement between the registrar and its clients that guarantees the clients legal protection of their intellectual property (to which the registrar's auditors will have access during the audits).
5. Discussion on permissible usage of the ISO 9001:2000 registration certificates is beyond the scope of this book—contact your registrar for details. As stated previously, only the organization's QMS is ISO 9001:2000 registered. It is not permissible to use the ISO 9001:2000 registration certificate to in any way imply that the software products of the organization are ISO 9001:2000 certified.
6. As an example, refer to the sample list of audit questions provided in appendix C.

10

Beyond Registration

Once the coveted goal of ISO 9000 registration has been achieved, it is important to remember that achievement of the registration does *not* represent the end of the organization's quality journey. Achievement of ISO 9000 registration can never be a final objective. On the contrary, it only signifies an important milestone in this journey. It is important always to keep in perspective what it really means to achieve ISO 9000 registration. An ISO 9000 registration provides independent confirmation that the organization has successfully established a sound QMS to enable it to deliver quality products and services, and to enable it to pursue the ultimate objective of continuous improvement, the quest for which is never ending.

Organizations have an obligation to use the tools for improvement that an ISO 9000–based QMS provides them; otherwise, they would have failed to meet a key objective of ISO 9000. Keep in mind that after achieving ISO 9000 registration, continued conformance to the standard's requirements will be periodically assessed by the organization's registrar, and continual improvement is a key clause of the standard because it promises the greatest returns on investment.

For an ISO 9000–registered organization, during the periodic surveillance audits, the registrar is particularly interested in assessing the organization for the following two items:

1. Is there evidence to confirm that the organization is continuing to deliver quality products and services in accordance with its QMS and ISO 9001:2000 requirements?

2. Is there evidence to confirm that the QMS is being continually improved?

Examples of relevant evidence the registrar may examine for this purpose include but are not limited to: results of customer satisfaction surveys, measurement data, and internal quality audit results. For example, if over a period of time the organization continues to uncover the same problems from its internal quality audits, it points to possible ineffective corrective and preventive action.

In the end, continuous improvement is about gradually increasing organizational maturity. ISO 9001:2000 provides organizations with a solid foundation for continuous improvement. It is not, and was not intended to be, a prescriptive guide to establish the perfect QMS. In fact, there is no such thing as a perfect QMS. There are no silver-bullet solutions when it comes to quality. Therefore, in order to fully leverage the QMS established as per ISO 9001:2000 requirements, organizations must build upon it. As an example, *ISO 9004:2000, Quality Management Systems—Guidelines for Performance Improvements,* may be used to further improve the effectiveness of the established QMS.

Appendix A
Quality Manual Outline

This appendix provides an outline for a quality manual that organizations can use as a template for creating their own quality manual.[1] The outline addresses both types of quality manuals introduced in chapter 3:

Appendix A.1: Process-Based Quality Manual, and

Appendix A.2: ISO 9001:2000–Based Quality Manual.

Note: Text included in brackets *<such as this>* is guidance text for using the template and is meant to be deleted from the completed quality manual.

APPENDIX A.1: QUALITY MANUAL OUTLINE (PROCESS-BASED)

Section 1: Introduction

- Purpose *<Describe the purpose of the quality manual>*

- Scope *<Describe the scope[2] of the QMS and the ISO 9001:2000 implementation, including a high-level description of the business processes and office locations covered. State business processes that could be assumed to be included within the scope of the ISO 9000 registration but are in fact excluded. Provide justification for permissible exclusions of ISO 9001:2000 requirements (as explained in chapter 3)>*

- Organizational Overview *<Provide a brief overview of the organization, its products, and its locations.>*

Section 2: QMS Overview

- Quality Policy *<Provide a statement of the organization's quality policy.>*

- Organization Chart *<Represent the organization's major functional areas (or departments) in an organization chart. Do not include names of employees in this organization chart, as such information is prone to change. Preferably, shade functional areas that are included in the scope of the ISO 9000 registration.>*

- Roles and Responsibilities *<Provide a brief description of the role and key responsibilities of each functional area in the organization chart (refer to explanation of subclause 5.5.1). Also provide a brief and generic description of responsibilities for a typical process owner.>*

- Management Representative *<Introduce the organization's management representative by name so employees are aware of the person in this key role. Briefly describe this person's responsibilities.>*

- Management Review of the QMS *<State who (role) participates in the periodic management review of the QMS, what is the periodicity of the management reviews, what is the quorum, and nature of items discussed at such reviews.>*

Section 3: QMS Structure

<Briefly describe the structure of the QMS, in terms of types of QMS documentation and their hierarchy. Following four-level hierarchy is widely used by ISO 9000 registered companies:>

- Level 1: Quality Manual

- Level 2: QMS Procedures

- Level 3: Work Instructions, Templates, Forms, Guidelines, Methods, and Checklists

- Level 4: Evidence of Use—Project Documents and Records

Section 4: QMS Content

- Brief Overview of ISO 9001:2000

- Overview of the Meta-Process *<Provide an overview of the organization's meta-process, and reference additional documentation, if any (such as process maps and procedures). Also briefly describe functional areas that are outside the SPDP, but part of the meta-process, such as: contracts and legal department(s); customer service; customer training; professional services; and others, as appropriate. Reference specific QMS procedures, if any, that further describe these functional areas.>*

- Overview of the Software Product Development Process

  - Product Release: Alpha, Beta, General Availability *<Identify the types of product releases (including criteria) and when they occur in the SPDP. Reference related QMS documentation, if any.>*

  - Milestone Reviews *<Identify the specific milestone reviews that are to be held. Reference related QMS documentation that specify the milestone review criteria for each milestone, including handling of deviations.>*

  - Configuration Management (CM) Baselines *<Identify the CM baselines and when they occur in the SPDP.>*

  - Management Processes: Management review of project progress; project management; product management *<Briefly describe management processes of the SPDP. Reference related QMS documentation, if any.>*

  - Software Development Lifecycle: System analysis; software requirements analysis; software design; implementation; integration test; system test; and others, as appropriate. *<Briefly describe SDLC processes. Reference related QMS documentation, if any.>*

  - Support Processes: Configuration management; quality assurance; software (and hardware) acquisition; infrastructure (including information technology); employee training; and others, as appropriate. *<Briefly describe support processes of the SPDP. Reference related QMS documentation, if any.>*

Section 5: ISO 9001:2000 to QMS Documentation Traceability Matrix

<Provide traceability between each requirements clause in ISO 9001:2000 and key QMS documentation (refer to explanation of subclause 5.4.2, and Table 5.2, page 105)>

Section 6: Related Documents

<Provide a list of all QMS documents referenced in the quality manual or otherwise related.>

APPENDIX A.2: QUALITY MANUAL OUTLINE (ISO 9001:2000–BASED)

Note: The only difference between an ISO 9001:2000–based quality manual and a process-based quality manual (outline for which is shown in appendix A.1) is the structure and content of "Section 4: QMS Content." All *other* sections in these two types of quality manuals may be *identical*. The outline of an ISO 9001:2000–based quality manual is as follows:

Section 1: Introduction

This section has the same structure and content as the process-based quality manual in Appendix A.1.

Section 2: QMS Overview

This section has the same structure and content as the process-based quality manual in Appendix A.1.

Section 3: QMS Structure

This section has the same structure and content as the process-based quality manual in Appendix A.1.

Section 4: QMS Content

- Brief Overview of ISO 9001:2000
- Clause 4: Quality management system requirements

<For clauses 4 to 8, and for each of the subclauses, provide a brief explanation of how the organization complies with the requirements in the clause (or subclause). Also provide references to supporting QMS documentation, as applicable.>

- – Subclause 4.1: General requirements
- – Subclause 4.2: Documentation requirements
- Clause 5: Management responsibility
  - – Subclause 5.1: Management commitment
  - – Subclause 5.2: Customer focus
  - – Subclause 5.3: Quality policy
  - – Subclause 5.4: Planning
  - – Subclause 5.5: Responsibility, authority and communication
  - – Subclause 5.6: Management review
- Clause 6: Resource management
  - – Subclause 6.1: Provision of resources
  - – Subclause 6.2: Human resources
  - – Subclause 6.3: Infrastructure
  - – Subclause 6.4: Work environment
- Clause 7: Product realization
  - – Subclause 7.1: Planning of product realization
  - – Subclause 7.2: Customer-related processes
  - – Subclause 7.3: Design and development
  - – Subclause 7.4: Purchasing
  - – Subclause 7.5: Production and service provision
  - – Subclause 7.6: Control of monitoring and measuring devices
- Clause 8: Measurement, analysis and improvement
  - – Subclause 8.1: General
  - – Subclause 8.2: Monitoring and measurement
  - – Subclause 8.3: Control of nonconforming product

- Subclause 8.4: Analysis of data

- Subclause 8.5: Improvement

Section 5: ISO 9001:2000 to QMS Documentation Traceability Matrix

This section has the same structure and content as the process-based quality manual in Appendix A.1.

Section 6: Related Documents

This section has the same structure and content as the process-based quality manual in Appendix A.1.

ENDNOTES

1. Additionally, you may also refer to *ISO/TR 10013:2001, Guidelines for quality management system documentation,* which offers guidance for writing a quality manual.
2. Note that the scope of the QMS and ISO 9001:2000 may or may not be the same. For example, an organization may choose to define business processes that are outside the scope ISO 9001:2000 requirements, but need to be documented because they are recognized by the organization as critical business processes, documentation of which makes good business sense.

Appendix B

Sample Templates and Forms

This appendix includes the following templates and forms:

B.1 Procedure Description Template

B.2 Product Requirements Document (System Specification) Template

B.3 Software Requirement Specification Template

B.4 Software Design Document Template

B.5 System Test Plan Template

B.6 Corrective Action Request Form

Note: Where necessary, guidance text for using the template is included in brackets *<such as this>*. It is meant to be deleted from the completed document.

B.1 PROCEDURE DESCRIPTION TEMPLATE

Section 1: Introduction

- Purpose *<Briefly describe the purpose of the process that this procedure describes.>*
- Scope *<Identify the scope of this process.>*

- Applicability *<Identify functional areas (departments) in the organization to which this procedure applies. This is to be used subsequently to identify relevant employees requiring training on this process.>*

- Terminology *<Only define terms that are specific to this document, or not otherwise defined in the organization's formally documented QMS Glossary.[1]>*

Section 2: Process Flowchart

<The flowchart should include all major activities or steps that are included in the process. Note that a flowchart may be omitted if the process flows sequentially, and providing a flowchart does not enhance readability and understanding.>

Section 3: Entry Criteria

<List all inputs and approvals that are necessary for the start of this process.>

Section 4: Input(s)

<List all inputs to this procedure and identify the process, procedure, role, or department providing the input.>

Section 5: Activity Descriptions

Activity Description	Output(s)	Responsible(s)
<Describe each major activity in a separate row. Ensure that the list of activity names matches those in the flowchart.>	*<List output(s) for each activity.>*	*<Identify role or department name that is responsible for performing the activity.>*

Section 6: Exit Criteria

<List all outputs and approvals that are necessary for the end of this process.>

Section 7: Output(s)

<List all outputs of this procedure and identify the process, procedure, role, or department receiving the output.>

Section 8: Process Metrics

<List process metrics that are used to measure, monitor, and continually improve this process.>

Section 9: Related Documents

<List other documents relevant to this procedure. These may include: templates, guidelines, checklists, and the like.>

Section 10: Document Change History

Document Version	Date	Change Performed By	Summary of Change
<Identify each document version.>	*<Identify the date each document version was created.>*	*<Identify who performed the change for each document version.>*	*<Provide a brief summary of changes for each document version.>*

B.2 PRODUCT REQUIREMENTS DOCUMENT (SYSTEM SPECIFICATION) TEMPLATE

Section 1: Introduction

- Purpose *<Describe the purpose of this document.>*
- Scope *<Describe the scope of this document.>*
- Prerequisites *<List the prerequisites necessary to understand the content of this document.>*
- Terminology *<List acronyms and definitions of terms.>*

Section 2: Product Overview

- Purpose of This Product (that is, overall system)
- Drivers for This Product *<List market and customer drivers that are behind the demand for this product.>*

- User Characteristics *<Describe pertinent characteristics of the users of this product, such as technical expertise and experience level.>*

Section 3: Product Description and Architecture

- Description of Product

- Product Context *<Describe if this is a stand-alone product or part of another system. Provide a context diagram for this product, where the product is depicted as a black box.>*

- Product Architecture *<Provide a high-level view of how the subsystems inside the product are organized.>*

- Description of Subsystems

Section 4: Product Capabilities

- Key Functional Requirements

- Operational Use-Case Scenarios

- Allocation of Key Functional Requirements to Subsystems

- Interface Requirements *<Specify external interface requirements, such as user interface, hardware interface, and software interface requirements>*

- Quality Requirements

- Product Documentation Requirements

Section 5: Project Issues

- Assumptions

- Technical Risks

- Design Constraints

Section 6: Requirements Traceability Matrix

<Trace each PRD requirement to the SRS that will elaborate on this requirement.>

Section 7: Related Documents

<Reference other specifications and third-party documents that are relevant to this document.>

Section 8: Document Change History

Document Version	Date	Change Performed By	Summary of Change
<Identify each document version.>	*<Identify the date each document version was created.>*	*<Identify who performed the change for each document version.>*	*<Provide a brief summary of changes for each document version.>*

B.3 SOFTWARE REQUIREMENT SPECIFICATION TEMPLATE

Section 1: Introduction

- Purpose *<Describe the purpose of this document.>*

- Scope *<Describe the scope of this document.>*

- Prerequisites *<List the prerequisites necessary to understand the content of this document.>*

- Terminology *<List acronyms and definition of terms.>*

Section 2: Software Product Overview

- Purpose of This Software Product

- Description of This Software Product

- Software Product Context *<Describe how and where this software product fits in the context of the overall product. >*

- Summary of Key Features of This Software Product

- Assumptions

- Technical Risks

- Design Constraints

Section 3: Software Requirements

- Functional Requirements

- Installation Requirements

- Configuration Requirements

- Interface Requirements *<Specify all external and internal software interface requirements>*

- Migration Requirements *<Specify other platforms and operating systems on which the product must operate.>*

- Security Requirements

- Software Test Tool Requirements *<Specify or reference the requirements for the software test tools needed to test the requirements.>*

- Product Documentation Requirements

- Training Requirements

- Quality Requirements

  - Performance Requirements

  - Reliability Requirements *< Describe the requirements pertaining to a certain guaranteed level of availability for the product, including recovery and restart after failure.>*

  - Maintainability Requirements *<Specify requirements that pertain to the ease of maintenance of the product.>*

  - *<Add other types of requirements as appropriate.>*

Section 4: Requirements Traceability Matrix

<Trace each SRS requirement to its parent PRD requirement. When an SRS requirement is not directly derived from a PRD requirement but is instead derived from another SRS requirement, then provide suitable explanation in the traceability matrix.>

<Trace each SRS requirement to the SDD that will contain the design for that requirement.>

Section 5: Related Documents

<Reference other specifications and third-party documents that are relevant to this document.>

Section 6: Document Change History

Document Version	Date	Change Performed By	Summary of Change
<Identify each document version.>	*<Identify the date each document version was created.>*	*<Identify who performed the change for each document version.>*	*<Provide a brief summary of changes for each document version.>*

B.4 SOFTWARE DESIGN DOCUMENT TEMPLATE

Section 1: Introduction

- Purpose *<Describe the purpose of this document.>*

- Scope *<Describe the scope of this document.>*

- Prerequisites *<List the prerequisites necessary to understand the content of this document.>*

- Terminology *<List acronyms and definitions of terms.>*

Section 2: Software Design Overview

- Software Design—Representation *<Provide a pictorial representation of the software design architecture, including software subsystems and their data and control interfaces. Provide static and dynamic representation, as appropriate.>*

- Software Design—Approach and Rationale *<Provide a brief rationale for the chosen architecture. If appropriate, briefly describe or reference alternate designs considered, and list advantage(s) of the chosen design.>*

- Software Subsystems (components)

Section 3: Software Design Details

- Software *<Subsystem 1>* Design

  - Input(s)

  - Processing *<Describe the processing performed in this subsystem. Describe the modules contained in this subsystem, or provide a reference to a lower-level design document that provides this information. For each module, describe the inputs, processing, outputs, and other pertinent information. If appropriate, also describe the dynamic behavior of the modules by means of timing diagrams.>*

  - Output(s)

  - Error Handling *<Describe types of errors that may occur, how they are detected, and handled.>*

- Software *<Subsystem 2>* Design

  - *<Describe same information as described for subsystem 1. Similarly, describe the design of all other software subsystems.>*

Section 4: Requirements Traceability Matrix

<Trace each design element to its parent SRS requirement.>

Section 5: Related Documents

<Reference other relevant documents, such as detailed software design schedule and personnel assignment.>

Section 6: Document Change History

Document Version	Date	Change Performed By	Summary of Change
<Identify each document version.>	*<Identify the date each document version was created.>*	*<Identify who performed the change for each document version.>*	*<Provide a brief summary of changes for each document version.>*

B.5 SYSTEM TEST PLAN TEMPLATE

Section 1: Introduction

- Purpose
- Scope
- Prerequisites
- Terminology

Section 2: Resources

- Test Equipment *<List the hardware test equipment (including emulators for the external environment), operating system (with patch levels), test tools, and system under test.>*
- Test Personnel
- Test Milestone Dates

Section 3: System Test Strategy and Methodology

- Scope of System Testing
- Entry Criteria
- Exit Criteria
- Test Limitations and Risk Mitigation *<State what requirements will not be tested and what alternate means will be used to validate the product against those requirements.>*

Section 4: System Test Case Summary

<In this section, list the different types of testing that will be performed, such as functional testing, interface testing, performance testing, use-case testing, and so on. For each type of test, provide a list of specific test cases that will be executed, along with a unique ID and brief description for each.>

Section 5: Requirements Traceability Matrix

<Provide complete traceability of PRD and/or SRS requirements to system test cases.>

Section 6: Related Documents

<Reference other relevant documents, such as detailed system test schedule and personnel assignment.>

Section 7: Document Change History

Document Version	Date	Change Performed By	Summary of Change
<Identify each document version.>	*<Identify the date each document version was created.>*	*<Identify who performed the change for each document version.>*	*<Provide a brief summary of changes for each document version.>*

B.6 CORRECTIVE ACTION REQUEST (CAR) FORM

CAR #	Severity: Major ☐ Minor ☐ Observation ☐	
Nonconformance Summary:		
Department/Process Audited:	Auditor:	Date:
Auditee Manager:		
Reference:		
ISO 9001:2000 Clause: *<Identify the clause against which the nonconformance is noted>*		
Quality Management System Document and Version: *<Identify the QMS document against which the nonconformance is noted. If the nonconformance is against a project plan document, then identify it here.>*		
Nonconformance Description:		
Description:		
Corrective Action Plan:		
Root Cause:		
Planned Corrective Action:		
Signature of Auditee's Supervisor:	Estimated date of completion:	
Approved by Auditor: Yes ☐ No ☐	Actual date of completion:	
Corrrective Action Follow-Up:		
Date of follow-up:		
Follow-up comments:		
Additional follow-up required? Yes ☐ No ☐	Date of additional follow-up (if applicable):	
CAR closed? Yes ☐ No ☐	Auditor:	

ENDNOTE

1. It is recommended that as part of the QMS documentation, a QMS glossary
   be formally documented and approved for organizationwide use. This will
   help facilitate a common understanding and consistent use of terminology
   in any communication and documentation pertaining to the QMS. Such a
   document is especially necessary in very large organizations, or with
   organizations with multiple locations.

Appendix C
Sample Audit Questions

Following is a sample list of typical auditor questions for each clause of ISO 9001:2000. This is not intended to be an exhaustive list; however, it provides sufficient examples of possible audit questions that may be asked during quality audits.

CLAUSE 4

Clause 4.1: Have you identified all the processes in your QMS, their sequence, and interactions?

Clause 4.1: Are any of your QMS processes outsourced to other supplier(s)? If yes, how do you control such processes?

Subclause 4.2.1: What is your documented quality policy?

Subclause 4.2.1: What are your documented quality objectives?

Subclause 4.2.2: Does your quality manual clearly specify the scope of your QMS?

Subclause 4.2.2: Does your quality manual describe how the processes in your QMS interact?

Subclause 4.2.2: Does your quality manual contain or reference documented procedures for the QMS?

Subclause 4.2.3: Are documents approved prior to use? How do you determine who needs to approve changes?

Subclause 4.2.3: Describe how you control document changes. Is this process formally documented?

Subclause 4.2.3: Are obsolete documents appropriately identified? How do you ensure they are not used?

Subclause 4.2.4: Do you have a procedure that describes how you control records?

Subclause 4.2.4: Where do you specify the retention time for each type of record?

CLAUSE 5

Clause 5.1: How does management ensure that quality objectives are established in the organization?

Clause 5.1: Are their periodic management reviews of the QMS?

Clause 5.2: How are customer requirements determined?

Clause 5.2: What verification do you perform to ensure that specific customer requirements have been met?

Clause 5.3: How do you communicate the quality policy to employees?

Clause 5.3: Are employees aware of the quality policy? Do they understand how it relates to their job?

Clause 5.3: Is the quality policy adhered to in the organization (or is it merely a marketing slogan)?

Subclause 5.4.1: Are the quality objectives quantitative (measurable)?

Subclause 5.4.1: Do employees know what quality objectives apply to their jobs?

Subclause 5.4.2: How does management ensure that the organization plans for achievement of defined quality objectives?

Subclause 5.4.2: How does management ensure that integrity of the QMS and compliance to ISO 9001:2000 requirements is maintained when there are changes to the QMS, or there are organizational changes that impact the QMS?

Subclause 5.5.1: Are organization responsibilities clearly defined and communicated? How is this done?

Subclause 5.5.2: Who is your management representative?

Subclause 5.5.3: Are employees informed about the effectiveness of the QMS? For example, are measurement data and customer satisfaction data communicated to relevant employees?

Subclause 5.6.1: What are some examples of typical agenda items for discussion at management reviews?

Subclause 5.6.2: Do management reviews follow up on the status of open action items from past management reviews?

Subclause 5.6.2: Are results of first-party, second-party, and third-party audits presented at management reviews?

Subclause 5.6.3: Are records of management reviews maintained, such as meeting minutes?

CLAUSE 6

Clause 6.1: Are there adequate resources to implement and maintain the QMS?

Clause 6.1: How are resources estimated and secured in a timely manner?

Subclause 6.2.1: Do employees have the needed competency to perform the job?

Subclause 6.2.2: Is the necessary competence for every employee position identified?

Subclause 6.2.2: Do you provide training or use other mechanisms to address deficiency in required competency in employees?

Subclause 6.2.2: How do you evaluate that the action taken to bridge the competency deficiency was effective?

Subclause 6.2.2: What records do you maintain of employee competency?

Clause 6.3: Is the infrastructure provided adequate for the task performed?

Clause 6.4: Is the work environment appropriately maintained?

CLAUSE 7

Clause 7.1: Is there a defined process for developing the product?

Clause 7.1: Are records maintained to demonstrate that the executed processes and developed product comply with applicable requirements?

Subclause 7.2.1: Are the requirements for the product adequately defined?

Subclause 7.2.2: Are the product requirements reviewed?

Subclause 7.2.2: Does the organization have the ability to meet the approved requirements?

Subclause 7.2.2: Are records maintained for the requirements reviews, including disposition of action items?

Subclause 7.2.3: What mechanisms do you use to communicate with the customer? Is this communication periodic or sporadic?

Subclause 7.2.3: Is the customer provided feedback on the status of customer complaints?

Subclause 7.3.1: How do you plan for design and development of a product?

Subclause 7.3.1: What mechanisms do you have in place to control project execution, manage interfaces between departments, and coordinate tasks?

Subclause 7.3.1: Are project plans revised, when appropriate, during the product development process?

Subclause 7.3.2: Are functional and nonfunctional requirements for the product defined?

Subclause 7.3.3: How are the design and development outputs documented? Are these approved prior to release?

Subclause 7.3.4: Is the design and development reviewed with appropriate parties during project execution as per plans?

Subclause 7.3.5: During project execution, is the design and development output verified against design and development input as per plans?

Subclause 7.3.6: Is the design and development validated against product requirements as per plans?

Subclause 7.3.7: In the event that a change to the design or development is required, is the change identified and approved prior to implementation?

Subclause 7.3.7: Is an assessment made of the impact of the proposed changes on the design and development already completed (or under way)?

Subclause 7.4.1: How do you ensure that the purchased product conforms to requirements?

Subclause 7.4.1: Is there a defined process and established criteria for the evaluation and selection of potential suppliers?

Subclause 7.4.2: Are the purchase requirements adequately defined?

Subclause 7.4.3: Is the purchased product verified against purchase requirements? How is the verification performed?

Subclause 7.5.1: Is the master copy of the software product uniquely identified and stored in a secure location?

Subclause 7.5.1: Are there controls in place to ensure that the replicated copy of the software product is a true copy of the master? Note: This question is only applicable if the product is delivered on physical media.

Subclause 7.5.2: When the software product is delivered without certain requirements being tested, are alternate means used to validate the product against those requirements?

Subclause 7.5.3: Has your organization determined need for traceability during product requirements? Can you show examples of traceability, such as traceability of test cases to requirements?

Subclause 7.5.4: How do you identify customer property?

Subclause 7.5.4: How do you protect customer property from unauthorized access and abuse, or corruption?

Subclause 7.5.5: How do you ensure that the product is adequately preserved during packaging and delivery to the customer?

Clause 7.6: Have you identified monitoring and measurement equipment requiring calibration? When and how is this calibration performed?

Clause 7.6: What calibration records do you maintain?

CLAUSE 8

Clause 8.1: Have you implemented measurements processes in your organization?

Subclause 8.2.1: Do you collect customer satisfaction information?

Subclause 8.2.1: How do you analyze and use customer satisfaction information for continual improvement?

Subclause 8.2.2: Do you have an internal audit plan?

Subclause 8.2.2: How many internal audits have you conducted?

Subclause 8.2.2: Are the internal auditors appropriately qualified and independent of the audited area?

Subclause 8.2.2: What records do you maintain of the audits performed? Do you present results of audits at management reviews?

Subclause 8.2.3: What process measurements do you use?

Subclause 8.2.4: What product measurements do you use?

Subclause 8.2.4: Can you show records that prove that the product meets the originally identified acceptance criteria?

Subclause 8.2.4: Can you show records to prove that the product was released by authorized personnel?

Clause 8.3: How do you control a product that is determined to be nonconforming?

Clause 8.3: What do you do if a product is determined to be nonconforming after release to the customer?

Clause 8.4: What techniques do you use to analyze measurement data?

Subclause 8.5.1: How do you continually improve the effectiveness of your QMS?

Subclause 8.5.2: Do you have a documented procedure for handling of corrective actions?

Subclause 8.5.2: Do you determine the root cause of nonconformities?

Subclause 8.5.2: How do you determine that a proposed corrective action is adequate?

Subclause 8.5.2: Do you maintain records of implemented corrective actions?

Subclause 8.5.3: Do you have a documented procedure for handling of preventive actions?

Subclause 8.5.3: Once a preventive action has been implemented, do you perform a follow-up to verify the implemented action?

Appendix D
Acronyms

The following table provides descriptions of all acronyms used in the book:

Acronym	Description
ABS	absolute value
	Definition: The absolute value of a number x, denoted by lxl, is the positive distance between the number and zero on the number line. In other words, it is the value of the corresponding "unsigned" number, that is, the number without the leading sign (+ or -). For example, the absolute value of -2, denoted by l-2l, is 2. The absolute value of 2, denoted by l2l, is also 2.
ANSI	American National Standards Institute
API	application programming interface
ASQ	American Society for Quality
CBT	computer-based training
CCB	configuration control board
CD	compact disc
CI	configuration item
CM	configuration management
CMMI	capability maturity model integration
COTS	commercial off-the-shelf (software)
CPI	cost performance index
EE	effort estimation
ESD	electrostatic discharge
FCA	functional configuration audit

Continued

Continued

Acronym	Description
FMEA	failure mode and effects analysis
GA	general availability (or generally available)
GQM	goal–question–metric
GUI	graphical user interface
HRS	hardware requirements specification
IATCA	International Auditor and Training Certification Association
ILT	instructor lead training
IRCA	International Register of Certified Auditors
ISO	International Organization for Standardization
IT	information technology
KLOC	thousand (K) lines of code
MoU	memorandum of understanding
MTBF	mean time between failure
MTTC	mean time to change
OJT	on-the-job training
PCA	physical configuration audit
PGM	process improvement group member
PP	planning precision
PRD	product requirements document
QMS	quality management system
RAB	Registrar Accreditation Board
RFI	request for information
RFQ	request for quotation (or quote)
SDD	software design document
SDLC	software development lifecycle
SEI	Software Engineering Institute (Pittsburgh)
SEPG	software engineering process group
SMART	specific, measurable, acceptable, realistic, time-bound
SPDP	software product development process
SRS	software requirements specification
TC	technical committee
WBT	Web-based training

References and Bibliography

ANSI/ISO/ASQ. *ANSI/ISO/ASQ 9001-2000: Quality management systems—requirements.* Milwaukee: ASQ Quality Press, 2000.

ANSI/ISO/ASQ. *ANSI/ISO/ASQ Q9000-2000: Quality managment standards—fundamentals and vocabulary.* Milwaukee: ASQ Quality Press, 2000.

Arter, D. "Beyond Compliance: An Examination of Compliance and Management Auditing." *Quality Progress* (June 2000).

Basili, V., and D. M. Weiss. "A Methodology for Collecting Valid Software Engineering Data." *IEEE Transactions on Software Engineering* 10, no. 3 (Nov. 1984).

Boehm, B. *Software Engineering Economics.* Englewood Cliffs, N.J.: Prentice Hall, 1982.

Boehm, B. "A Spiral Model for Software Development and Enhancement." *Computer* 21, no. 5 (1988): 61–72.

CMMI. *Capability Maturity Model Integration* (CMMI). Pittsburgh: Software Engineering Institute, Carnegie Mellon University, 2002.

Conte, S. D. et al. *Software Engineering Metrics and Models.* Boston: Benjamin Cummings, 1986.

Dalfonso, Maureen. *ISO 9000: Achieving Compliance and Certification.* New York: John Wiley and Sons, 1995.

Daskalantonakis, Michael. "A Practical View of Software Measurement and Implementation Experiences within Motorola." *IEEE Transactions on Software Engineering* 18, no. 11 (November 1992).

Fagan, M. "Advances in Software Inspections." *IEEE Transactions on Software Engineering* 12, no. 7 (1986).

Foster, T. *Managing Quality: An Integrative Approach.* Englewood Cliffs, N.J.: Prentice Hall, 2000.

IEEE 730-2002. *IEEE Standard for Software Quality Assurance Plans.* New York: IEEE, 2002.

IEEE Std. 828-1998. *Standard for Software Configuration Management Plans.* New York: IEEE, 1998.

International Organization for Standardization (ISO). 1, rue de Varembé, Case postale 56, CH-1211 Geneva 20, Switzerland. www.iso.ch. Phone: +41 22 749 01 11. Fax: +41 22 733 34 30. E-mail: central@iso.ch.

ISO. *ISO/TR 10013: 2001.Guidelines for quality management systems documentation.* Geneva, Switzerland: International Organization for Standardization, 2001.

ISO. *ISO 10005:1995 Quality management—guidelines for quality plans.* Geneva, Switzerland: International Organization for Standardization, 1995.

ISO. *BSR/ISO/ASQ QE19011-2002 Guidelines for quality and/or environmental management systems auditing.* Milwaukee: ASQ Quality Press, 2002.

ISO. *ISO FDIS 90003 Software and system engineering—guidelines for the application of ISO 9001:2000 to computer software,* FDIS. Geneva, Switzerland: International Organization for Standardization, 2003.

ISO Survey. *The ISO survey of ISO 9000 and ISO 14000 certificates, 11th cycle.* Geneva, Switzerland: International Organization for Standardization, 2001.

ISO/IEC. *ISO/IEC 12207: 1995* and *Amd. 1: 2002, Information technology— software life cycle processes.* Geneva, Switzerland: International Organization for Standardization, 1995.

Jalote, Pankaj. "Use of Metrics in High-Maturity Organizations." *Software Quality Professional* 4, no. 2 (2002).

Johnson, K. "It's Fun to Work with F-M-E-A." *Quality Progress* (January 2002).

Jones, C. Keynote address: Fifth International Conference of Software Quality, Austin, Texas, 1995.

Kaplan, R., and D. Norton. "The Balanced Scorecard: Measures that Drive Performance." *Harvard Business Review* (January 1992).

Kehoe, Raymond, and Alka Jarvis. *ISO 9000-3: A Tool for Software Product and Process Improvement.* New York: Springer, 1995.

Ketola, Jeanne, and Kathy Roberts. "Demystifying ISO 9001:2000." *Quality Progress* (September and October 2001).

Liebesman, S., and J. Mroz. "ISO 9001: 2000 Experiences: First Results Are In." *Quality Pro*gress (April 2002).

Nanda, V. "On Tailoring an Organizational Standard Software Development Process for Specific Projects." In *Proceedings of the 11th International Conference on Software Quality*, Pittsburgh, 2001.

―――. *Quality Management System Implementation Handbook for Product Development Companies.* Boca Raton: CRC Press, Forthcoming.

Pressman, R. *Software Engineering: A Practitioner's Handbook.* New York: McGraw Hill, 1996.

Ratikin, S. "Creating Accurate Estimates and Realistic Schedules." *Software Quality Professional* 4, no. 2 (2002).

Rubin, H., et al. "The U.S. Software Industry." *IEEE Software* (January 2002).

van Veenendaal, E., et al. "Measuring Software Product Quality." *Software Quality Professional* 5, no. 1 (2002).

Vavra, Terry. "ISO 9001:2000 and Customer Satisfaction." *Quality Progress* (May 2002).

Index